*This book was written with our families in mind:
our wives, children, grandchildren and siblings.
We hope enough has been learned so that none of them
will ever experience a tragedy on the scale of COVID-19
in their lifetimes.*

Prologue

When examining the COVID pandemic from a historical perspective, it is helpful to study the description of past pandemics. There have been many that have changed history, but this is unquestionably the most famous written description of a pandemic with monumental consequences for the world.

In 431 BC, the Peloponnesian War broke out between the two leading city-states of Greece: Athens and Sparta. In an early phase of the war, Sparta laid siege to Athens, and many of the citizens of the rural areas outside of Athens moved into the city for protection. In 430 BC, a great plague that originated in Ethiopia struck the "virgin soil" of Athens. Most of the crowded city became infected including the great statesman, Pericles, who along with his two sons died of the plague (a key event in the ultimate victory of Sparta.) The epidemic came in three waves – in 430 BC, again in the summer of 428 BC, and a third wave in the winter of 427-426 BC. In the ensuing five years 75,000 to 100,000 people, more than one-quarter of the population of Athens, died. The disease that actually caused the plague has never been identified and has been the subject of speculation for decades. Whatever the cause, the great Athenian general and historian Thucydides (who contracted the plague but survived) left a meticulous eye-witness account and wrote a description of the situation, detailing not only the physical but the social consequences, which remains a classic more than 2500 years later.

Mt Sinai J Med 76:456-467, 2009. (c) 2009 Mount Sinai School of Medicine.

The Text

The following narrative comes from the History of the Peloponnesian War, II.vii.3-54 as translated by scholar P. J. Rhodes and given by Michael Grant in his *Readings in the Classical Historians*.

[The plague] is said to have broken out previously in many other places, in the region of Lemnos and elsewhere, but there was no previous record of so great a pestilence and destruction of human life. The doctors were unable to cope, since they were treating the disease for the first time and in ignorance: indeed, the more they came into contact with sufferers, the more liable they were to lose their own lives. No other device of men was any help. Moreover, supplication at sanctuaries, resort to divination, and the like were all unavailing. In the end, people were overwhelmed by the disaster and abandoned efforts against it.

The plague is said to have come first of all from Ethiopia beyond Egypt and from there it fell on Egypt and Libya and on much of the [other] lands. It struck the city of Athens suddenly. People in the Piraeus caught it first, and so, since there were not yet any fountains there, they actually alleged that the Peloponnesians had put poison in the wells. Afterwards, it arrived in the upper city too, and then deaths started to occur on a much larger scale. Everyone, whether doctor or layman, may say from his own experience what the origin of it is likely to have been, and what causes he thinks had the power to bring about so great a change. I shall give a statement of what it was like, which people can study in case it should ever attack again, to equip themselves with foreknowledge so that they shall not fail to recognize it. I can give this account because I both suffered the disease myself and saw other victims of it.

It was universally agreed that this particular year was exceptionally free from disease as far as other afflictions were concerned. If people did first suffer from other illnesses, all ended in this. Others were caught with no warning, but suddenly, when they were in good health. The disease began with a strong fever in the head and reddening and burning in the eyes; the first internal symptoms were that the throat and tongue became bloody and the breath unnatural and malodorous. This was followed by sneezing and hoarseness, and in a short time the affliction descended to the chest, producing violent coughing. When it became established in the heart, it convulsed that and produced every kind of evacuation of bile known to the doctors, accompanied by great discomfort. Most victims then suffered from empty retching, which induced violent convulsion: they abated after this for some sufferers, but only much later for others.

The exterior of the body was not particularly hot to the touch or yellow, but was reddish, livid, and burst out in small blisters and sores. But inside the burning was so strong that the victims could not bear to put on even the lightest clothes and linens, but had to go naked, and gained the greatest relief by plunging into cold water. Many who had no one to keep watch on them even plunged into wells, under the pressure of insatiable thirst; but it made no difference whether they drank a large quantity or a small. Throughout the course of the disease, people suffered from sleeplessness and inability to rest. For as long as the disease was raging, the body did not waste away, but held out unexpectedly against its suffering. Most died about the seventh or the ninth day from the beginning of the internal burning, while they still had some strength. If they escaped then, the disease descended to the belly: there violent ulceration and totally fluid diarrhea occurred, and most people then died from the weakness caused by that.

The disease worked its way right through the body from the top, beginning with the affliction which first settled in the head. If anyone survived the worst *symptoms, the disease left its mark by catching his extremities. It attacked the privy parts, and the fingers and toes, and many people survived but lost these, while others lost their eyes. Others, on first recovering, suffered a total loss of memory, and were unable to recognize themselves and their relatives.*

The nature of the disease was beyond description, and the sufferings that it brought to each victim were greater than human nature can bear. There is one particular point in which it showed that it was unlike the usual run of illnesses: the birds and animals which feed on human flesh either kept away from the bodies, although there were many unburied, or if they did taste them it proved fatal. To confirm this, there was an evident shortage of birds of that kind, which were not to be seen either near the victims or anywhere else. What happened was particularly noticeable in the case of dogs, since they live with human beings.

Apart from the various unusual features in the different effects which it had on different people, that was the general nature of the disease. None of the other common afflictions occurred at that time; or any that did ended in this. Some victims were neglected and died; others died despite a great deal of care. There was not a single remedy, you might say, which ought to be applied to give relief, for what helped one sufferer harmed another. No kind of constitution, whether strong or weak, proved sufficient against the plague, but it killed off all, whatever regime was used to care for them. The most terrifying aspect of the whole affliction was the despair which resulted when someone realized that he had the disease: people immediately lost hope, and so through their attitude of mind were much more likely to let themselves go and not hold out. In addition, one person caught the disease through caring for another, and so they died like sheep: this was the greatest cause of loss of life. If people were afraid and unwilling to go near to others, they died in isolation, and many houses lost all their occupants through the lack of anyone to care for them. Those who did go near to others died, especially those with any claim to virtue, who from a sense of honor did not spare themselves in going to visit their friends, persisting when in the end even the members of the family were overcome by the scale of the disaster and gave up their dirges for the dead.

Those who had come through the disease had the greatest pity for the suffering and dying, since they had previous experience of it and were now feeling confident for themselves, as the disease did not attack the same person a second time, or at any rate not fatally. Those who recovered were congratulated by the others, and in their immediate elation cherished the vain hope that for *the future they would be immune to death from any other disease.*

The distress was aggravated by the migration from the country into the city, especially in the case of those who had themselves made the move. There were no houses for them, so they had to live in stifling huts in the hot season of the year, and destruction raged unchecked. The bodies of the dead and dying were piled on one another and people at the point of death reeled about the streets and around all the springs in their passion to find water. The sanctuaries in which people were camping were filled with corpses, as deaths took place even there: the disaster was overpowering, and as people did not know what would become of them, they tended to neglect the sacred and the secular alike. All the funeral customs which had previously been observed were thrown into confusion and the dead were buried in any way possible. Many who lacked friends, because so many had died before them, turned to shameless forms of disposal: some would put their own dead on someone else's pyre, and set light to it before those who had prepared it could do so themselves; others threw the body they were carrying on to the top of another's pyre when it was already alight, and slipped away.

In other respects, too, the plague marked the beginning of a decline to greater lawlessness in the city.

People were more willing to dare to do things which they would not previously have admitted to enjoying, when they saw the sudden changes of fortune, as some who were prosperous suddenly died, and their property was immediately acquired by others who had previously been destitute. So they thought it reasonable to concentrate on immediate profit and pleasure, believing that their bodies and their possessions alike would be short- lived. No one was willing to persevere in struggling for what was considered an honorable result, since he could not be sure that he would not perish before he achieved it. What was pleasant in the short term, and what was in any way conducive to that, came to be accepted as honorable and useful. No fear of the gods or law of men had any restraining power, since it was judged to make no difference whether one was pious or not as all alike could be seen dying. No one expected to live long enough to have to pay the penalty for his misdeeds: people tended much more to think that a sentence already decided was hanging over them, and that before it was executed, they might reasonably get some enjoyment out of life. So the Athenians had fallen into the great misfortune and were being ground down by it, with people dying inside the city and the land being laid waste outside. (II.vii.3-54)

Acknowledgments

The person most central to the publication of this book was Sid Tepps, our resident IT genius. When writing a book today, it is essential to be proficient with current computer software and hardware. We were not; he certainly was, and like the skilled quarterback guiding the team, he directed the words onto the page to create a finished product. It was no small accomplishment, and our gratitude to Sid cannot be overstated. Matt Fuller was our art director and coordinator, and his advice and guidance was also essential.

On the writing side, Dr. Mary Hall, a fine pediatrician, co-authored several chapters on pediatric vaccines and COVID-19. Her insights and observations made this a more comprehensive book, especially because this aspect of the contagion was so important. We want to thank Linda Black and Sue Franklin, who both did a careful reading of the material and offered thoughtful criticism. Rose Ippolito did her usual excellent job of indexing, truly a master of her craft.

Finally, thanks to Bruce Dold, who provided several smart thoughts for topics to cover throughout the pandemic. And especially John McCormick, who did a nonpareil job of editing both ideas and copy. There aren't many as good at doing this as he is, and his efforts made this book far better than it would have been otherwise.

Introduction

There is something beautiful about ignorance...as long as one has the desire to expand the limits of their knowledge so that ignorance remains ephemeral. Oxymoronic as it may be, being wrong leads us to a better understanding of the world and ourselves.

— Nobel laureate Richard Feynman

It was raining on July 4, 2021 in Provincetown, Massachusetts. A seemingly minor detail, but it took on huge significance because it contributed to one of the most consequential days of the COVID-19 pandemic.

Provincetown is a small resort community, which attracts thousands of partygoers every Independence Day. The previous year, 2020, was a low point because it was during the first wave of the COVID-19 epidemic, which made Provincetown a relative ghost town that summer. Even though COVID-19 was still raging throughout the country a year later in 2021, the COVID-19 vaccine had been released early that year. Visitors, now fully vaccinated, returned *en masse* to party. The rain kept the partygoers inside but they massed in bars, restaurants and clubs - undeterred because the Centers for Disease Control and Protection (CDC), along with most experts, believed the new COVID-19 vaccine would protect against infection and transmission of the virus.

That turned out to be wrong. Almost immediately, a COVID-19 outbreak hit the vaccinated community. It was soon clear that vaccinated individuals could not only contract COVID-19 but transmit it as well.

"This was absolutely a key moment and a bit of a turning point, certainly in our thinking," said Bronwyn MacInnis, the director of genomic surveillance at the Broad Institute of MIT and Harvard. "It just showed us that there was more to come, and the virus had more tricks up its sleeve."

As it turned out, vaccination decreased but did not eliminate the chances of contracting or transmitting COVID-19. Other factors such as viral load, exposure time, and personal immunity were critical variables. And vaccinated individuals who did contract COVID-19 almost invariably had milder infections, which meant that vaccination saved many lives, in the U.S. and around the world.

But the Provincetown experience shattered the conventional wisdom that mass vaccination would shut down COVID-19 transmission and summarily end the pandemic. The CDC was forced to backtrack quickly, revise its advice, and change guidelines on transmission. Among other things, this led to new recommendations on masking, which remain controversial to this day. Just as important was the damage to the credibility of the health agency, the media, and leading experts, which all have yet to recover completely.

That story, and those repercussions, embody one of the themes of this book: Error is part of science (and of science journalism). What is thought to be true today may not be true tomorrow, and placing too much confidence in today's truths can have serious unintended consequences. We know more today than we did yesterday – but only if we learn from yesterday's mistakes. It is important to correct errors as soon as possible, but never to deny them.

Since this book tells the story of COVID-19 as it happened in the first four years of the pandemic, some things you read here turned out wrong. Several of the early chapters in this book now seem overly parochial – concerns about how the pandemic will affect Chicago and Illinois. That's because our initial impression in early spring 2020 was that the contagion would be primarily regional. It did hit the Northeast and then the Midwest initially, but by the summer it was obvious COVID-19 was going to be a major national problem, just as it had been in Western Europe. Our initial optimism about limited regional spread proved naive.

Other things are waiting to be found in error in the future – and some undoubtedly will. This is where Richard Feynman's observation about constructive ignorance comes in. Looking back at the pandemic as things actually occurred provides perspective that is not available in the rewrites of history – and as people try to justify their actions, rewrites of history are inevitable. You are guaranteed to see that happen in future COVID-19 accounts. Rather than a sanitized future version of the COVID-19 outbreak, a contemporaneous recounting "leads us to a better understanding of the world and ourselves" as Feynman put it. Which is why it was vital to write a book consisting of columns of just what was going on at the time.

Many of the articles in this book were op-ed commentaries first published by the Chicago Tribune, which has been one of the nation's, and in fact one of the world's, beacons of science journalism in the fog of the COVID-19 contagion. The editorial page, run by Chris Jones and his excellent staff solicited our thoughts on the pandemic, without regard to politics or conventional wisdom. Unlike editors at some publications, they never promoted an agenda, especially on controversial topics, and never edited our copy along those lines. They are to be commended for their editorial stance along scientific lines, and it is no exaggeration to say this book would not have been possible without them.

This, then, is the story of COVID-19 in the US that began on January 19, 2020, when a 35-year-old man presented to an urgent care clinic in Snohomish County,

Washington, with a four-day history of cough after returning from a trip to Wuhan, China. He became the first known case of COVID-19 in this country (although almost certainly there were cases under the radar before that). That fortunate man survived; since then more than a million have not. This book is dedicated to their memory.

Table of Contents

GRIM PESSIMISM & QUESTIONS

EMERGING HOPE

THE VIRUS STRIKES BACK

RECOVERING & LEARNING TO COEXIST

REFLECTIONS & PROJECTIONS

EPILOGUE

Doctors' advice: What we can do now to slow the coronavirus

Robert A· Weinstein Cory Franklin *Chicago Tribune*
3·15·20

As Chicago and other communities across the U.S. and around the world put drastic measures in place to control the coronavirus pandemic, many questions have arisen about what else we can do — individually, by our public officials and within the medical community — to keep ourselves safe. As physicians, one of whom specializes in infectious diseases, we offer basic guidance.

Since the turn of this century, the world has faced three respiratory illness epidemics caused by the coronavirus. The first, SARS, came from a live food market in China in 2003. Because there was limited community spread, basic isolation measures kept the worldwide SARS case number around 8,000, albeit with a 10% mortality rate. In 2012, MERS emerged as a localized Middle East problem, related in large part to human exposure to camels. The U.S. escaped unscathed from these initial epidemics. Our luck, and that of the rest of the world, ran out in late 2019. The third epidemic coronavirus, COVID-19, like its cousin SARS, emanated from a live food market in China and spread quickly to humans.

The good news is that COVID-19 respiratory infections are less lethal than SARS; the bad news is they are far more contagious. Despite aggressive isolation and quarantine programs, COVID-19 spread widely in China and then to more than 129 countries via plane and cruise ship passengers. The spread by patients with minimal symptoms — infected, but in the community — has created a risk of extensive dissemination similar to that of influenza.

With more than 150,000 cases of COVID-19 worldwide and over 2,500 (and rising) in the U.S., a clear clinical picture is emerging: about 80% of infections are mild to moderate; the rest will be moderate to severe with an overall fatality rate of about 2%. The death rate increases dramatically to 10- 20% in the highest-risk patients — those older than 60 and those with underlying chronic medical diseases. It is below 1% in young, healthy patients. The overall mortality will drop as testing identifies less severe cases, but even an overall fatality rate of 1% is 10 times more lethal than seasonal influenza. If just 10% of the American populace acquired COVID-19, a 1% fatality rate would still mean more than 300,000 deaths.

In the absence of a vaccine and/or effective antiviral agents, control of COVID-19 would traditionally rely on prompt case recognition through extensive diagnostic testing, aggressive contact tracing, isolation of those testing positive, quarantine of exposed individuals and use of protective gear by heath care workers. But the preliminary experience in China and now in Italy, Seattle and New Rochelle, New York, has demonstrated that basic public health measures are insufficient.

While more aggressive approaches such as closing public venues, limiting meetings and canceling parades will cause significant economic disruption, lives will be saved in at least two ways: fewer new cases especially among those at highest risk, and the surge of cases will be blunted, diminishing the possibility of overwhelming the health care system.

Individuals:

What can you do personally? Adhere to public health advice: avoid crowds; work from home if possible; if you are in a high-risk group, have others do your grocery shopping; wash your hands frequently (soap and water for at least 20 seconds), disinfect frequently touched surfaces with wipes or sprays, and use alcohol hand gel as well.

Surgical masks? They work — that is why healthcare workers wear them — but they may become contaminated during use. They shield from the respiratory droplets that spread COVID-19, which can travel up to six feet through the air, the basis for social distancing recommendations. The CDC is not currently recommending masks outside of health care settings, but if you decide to wear a mask on public transportation, in close spaces or near coughers, shortages will mean that you will likely need to reuse your mask, as long as it is dry and intact. Look up information from reputable public health websites on the correct way to wear it.

Public officials:

What can our leaders, local and national, do? In the short term, the widened availability of diagnostic testing and the proposed economic relief package by Congress are a start. Government should ensure availability of basics — food, medications, toiletries — in the face of panic buying. In the long term, they should rework the systems for developing, approving and deploying diagnostic tests to create the surge capacity that this epidemic mandates.

Medical community:

What can the medical community do? Every hospital should guarantee that its triage and patient care systems, staffing, equipment and supplies are prepared to handle the likely onslaught. This preparation may include temporarily controlling facility access, limiting visitors and canceling elective procedures. Medical researchers should perform fast-track testing for antiviral medications, which have been useful for influenza treatment. Ideally, we need a vaccine for coronaviruses writ large, though in the best case situation that could be at least a year away.

Schools, from universities to kindergartens, have closed, but we will need more data to decide for how long, given the wide-ranging implications of school closings. Children have been minimally affected by this virus, but we don't know if they can be Trojan horses, bringing COVID-19 home and to the wider community.

Other questions abound. How long will this last? Will warmer weather put an end to the spread? Will this become an ongoing or seasonal problem like flu? Will we be watching the Cubs and White Sox this summer? More diagnostic testing will soon give us some estimates on the extent and rate of community spread. It's hard to know, but don't panic and hopefully we will all be back in the stands by the summer.

As we flatten the curve, a new pandemic role for the McCormick Place field hospital?

Cory Franklin *Chicago Tribune* 4·17·20

We are well into the first phase of the COVID-19 pandemic, with the stunning number of cases and deaths still rising, albeit at a slower pace than weeks ago. Our hospitals have experienced tremendous strains, but heroically, they have not buckled under the surge of cases and we have not run short of ventilators. Gov. J.B. Pritzker has said he is cautiously optimistic, given a stable rate of positive virus tests and the fact that hospitalizations, ventilator use and intensive care beds dedicated to COVID-19 patients have appeared to have leveled off.

So whither McCormick Place?

The U.S. Army Corps of Engineers, the Illinois National Guard and local contractors transformed much of the exhibit space into a makeshift field hospital in a remarkably short period of time, anticipating an overflow of COVID-19 patients. Ventilators are arriving, staff is trained and the convention center is on track to be able to accept 3,000 acute patients — who may never show up. We have managed to avoid the problem of exceeding hospital capacity so far, but that does not mean McCormick Place should be all dressed up with no place to go.

Instead of relieving area hospitals by accepting overflow COVID-19 admissions as originally planned, the Near South Side convention center can help out the hospitals by accepting COVID-19 discharges who are still too sick to return home. It wasn't what was originally planned, but McCormick Place can serve primarily as an outflow release for discharges rather than an intake for admissions.

A step in that direction came Friday, with the announcement that five patients had been moved to the makeshift field hospital. Dr. Ngozi Ezike, director of the Illinois Department of Public Health, said all the patients at McCormick were "deemed appropriate to leave the hospital and not quite ready to go home." Most of the major hospital ICUs in the area are seeing better survival rates than what had been previously reported in Europe as we gain experience with the complications of the coronavirus. (British Prime Minister Boris Johnson is the most recent high-profile example of an ICU survivor of COVID-19.) Moving into the second phase of the pandemic, we are faced with a number of new questions, including where to place COVID-19 hospital survivors who are still too sick to return home and may still be contagious.

That problem is particularly important to area hospitals and intensive care units, which, while not filled to capacity, must expect new waves of patients and don't have the luxury of holding patients for the weeks needed to recover. They must also make space for acute non-COVID emergencies and postoperative patients. Many of the COVID-19 ICU survivors, and some of the other hospitalized COVID-19 patients, are debilitated due to advanced age or chronic disease. They still require continued medical care and in many cases physical and/or respiratory therapy, which they cannot receive at home. Some are candidates for skilled nursing facilities or rehabilitation centers, but there may not be enough spots for all these patients — and in some cases the institutions are reluctant to accept them given their own problems with the coronavirus.

To accommodate these patients, McCormick Place would need stringent infection- control measures, rapid on-site virus testing for everyone — staff and patients — who enters the building, and the right mix of personnel. More primary doctors but fewer specialists than previously anticipated, and perhaps more nurses and therapists than were originally planned. Not as much high-tech, but more high-touch (with gloves and protective equipment, of course). Going forward, providing for survivors of COVID-19 may be the saving grace of McCormick Place.

Besides offering the care these patients so desperately need, it can serve as a clearinghouse for patterns of recovery and testing. There is much information to be gained on how long patients remain virus positive and when they revert to negative, and if and when survivors develop antibodies to the virus. This will mean an essential role for infectious disease specialists and epidemiologists at the convention center. In addition, there would have to be close coordination with the area hospitals for laboratory data, medical records and follow-up visits. McCormick Place is obviously not the long-term answer for these patients. It is simply a holdover location until some patients can return home, others can be accommodated by nursing homes and rehab centers and other facilities can be set up for continuing care.

I have retired from active duty, but my brave ICU colleagues, who are currently taking care of the sickest COVID-19 patients on a daily basis, say they are seeing clinical syndromes that they have never seen before. They tell me flexibility is the key; plans must change on the fly. The pandemic is teaching us to imagine, learn and improvise.

The Nobel laureate Richard Feynman, one of the greatest scientists of the 20th century, once said, "It is not unreasonable that we grapple with problems ... our responsibility is to do what we can, improve the solutions and pass them on." The field hospital at McCormick Place is still indispensable, it's just that it may take on a role different from the one we first planned for.

Overwhelmed by the COVID-19 data? Here are 8 rules for understanding the numbers

Cory Franklin *Chicago Tribune* 4·28·20

During the coronavirus epidemic, it's easy to become overwhelmed by data — confirmed cases, deaths per million, case-fatality rates, etc· They are imprecise numbers that are often misquoted or quoted out of context· This, in turn, generates political pronouncements, scientific observations and media punditry that is frequently wrong, but rarely uncertain· Obtaining accurate information can be like drinking from a fire hose· So much information, what to believe? Here are eight tips on how to consider the numbers related to the coronavirus pandemic:

All models are wrong· Some are useful. Models are mathematical descriptions of the real world used for calculations and predictions. They depend on assumptions and the numbers entered. Every model is an imperfect tool, some more than others. This is evident from the wide variance in predictions of COVID-19 deaths, from several million to the current figure nearing 60,000, which we will surpass shortly. Politicians use models to formulate policy, but models are always incomplete and wise policymakers must understand this. No single model should ever be accepted as the final word.

Long-range projections are typically less accurate than short-range projections. It's easier to predict tomorrow's weather than it is to predict next week's. Conditions are always changing, and forecasters must account for uncertainty, make assumptions and anticipate unknowable future events. In the coronavirus pandemic different countries use different models and develop different strategies. Great Britain changed its policy midstream when scientists revised their models.

Numbers are a representation of reality, not reality itself. The point of numbers is to help understand the reality of what's happening. A philosopher once said, "the map is not the territory," meaning there is a difference between a description of something and the thing itself. A good example of using numbers but ignoring reality was how some people describe COVID-19 as not much worse than the flu, based on the number of deaths from both. The comparison is inapt; flu deaths are a roughly defined estimate per season derived from multiple projections. In contrast, COVID-19 deaths have actually been observed over a period of weeks, and most deaths are clearly attributable to the virus (though not all). Only rarely has seasonal flu forced the creation of temporary field hospitals and morgues. The coronavirus is clearly not the routine seasonal flu.

Numbers require context. Adjust numbers to the size of the population. California illustrates how case numbers and deaths should be normalized to the size of the population. California is fifth in the number of total cases in the United States, but 30th in cases per capita. The state remains a mystery as to why it has a dramatically lower caseload and death total than expected, normalized for its size.

There is no perfect number. No number is exact; every number is subject to the limitations of measurement. The number of cases of COVID-19 is far from precise — it is an obvious undercount because not everyone has been tested. But it is a useful number for establishing trends. Likewise, some death figures are overcounts, others are undercounts and no one can say which predominates or by how much. But the measured number is a reliable, uniform outcome and helps us understand these trends, which is our ultimate goal. Rather than automatically discarding imperfect numbers as some advocate, try to understand their imperfections when looking at them.

Trends are more important than single values. The coronavirus has proved unpredictable — what was true yesterday may not be true today. It is tempting to pick out a single number and draw conclusions, but a single value may prove to be an outlier. To observe trends, information is more accurate when it is collected over time. A single value is a snapshot, many values over time are a movie.

Beware of cherry-picking. We are often treated to articles with headlines such as "What the U.S. can learn from some other country" or "What one state got right." No two regions are completely comparable — every region has a different population, climate, policy and a different situation. It's tempting to select some place to illustrate a point that does not hold up under scrutiny. Canada is widely praised for its approach to the pandemic, but the Canadian profile of cases and deaths is similar to that of South Carolina, which has been excoriated for its approach. Similar numbers, different interpretation.

Known knowns. Then Secretary of Defense Donald Rumsfeld explained the uncertainty of complex situations when he said of the Iraq War, "As we know, there are known knowns; there are things we know we know. We also know there are known unknowns; that is to say we know there are some things we do not know. But there are also unknown unknowns — the ones we don't know we don't know."

Among the known unknowns in the uncertainty of the coronavirus epidemic are how the virus is transmitted and especially how it is transmitted by asymptomatic carriers; whether recovery means immunity to the virus;

whether viral transmission will be deterred by warm weather; whether antivirals currently being tested will be effective; whether a timely vaccine can be developed; and how many people in the United States actually carry the virus. The unknown unknowns? There are many, and we don't even know what they are.

There are pitfalls everywhere in determining what's happening. When reading about this pandemic, don't be discouraged. No one, anywhere, has all the answers.

Illinois can safely start to reopen, if we follow these measures

Robert A. Weinstein Cory Franklin *Chicago Tribune*
5·18·20

Three early lessons from the COVID-19 epidemic:

Tight lockdown is workable as a short-term strategy but loses effectiveness and brings unintended consequences over time.

The idea that society cannot resume until we find a vaccine is unrealistic because a vaccine is not guaranteed.

It is harder to sit on the couch and watch six hours of television than commonly thought — especially without sports.

As weeks turn to months, with the increasingly warm weather, tension is palpable. People want their lives and livelihoods back; more churchgoers are defying instructions to skip services and too many among us are redefining "personal responsibility to my community" as "I've had enough of this."

Yet Illinois is in a particularly precarious position. The inconvenient truth is that Illinois has become a national hot spot. Third in total COVID-19 cases after New York and New Jersey, Illinois will be the next state to reach 100,000 cases. Only ten countries in the world rank ahead of Illinois in number of cases. Fortunately, our death total is not especially high; for some reason mortality in Illinois is below the national average.

Why is Illinois, and especially Chicago, performing worse than some states, such as Georgia, that have reopened widely? Nothing is certain, but here are two likely explanations: failure to control the spread in Illinois nursing homes (a failure that also doomed thousands of New Yorkers) and inattention to social distancing. Parties and spontaneous group gatherings may have led to new chains of infection transmission in the past month.

How can we regain control and reopen safely? Some steps are absolutely essential: Ensure as much safety as possible for the elderly and high-risk (more than 90% of deaths in Illinois are in high-risk patients with such underlying conditions as diabetes and obesity), prevent large gatherings and decontaminate public transportation assiduously. We must pay special attention to hospitals and jails (so far, Cook County Jail has performed commendably in bringing its outbreak under control).

The most important measure may be far greater transparency with what is happening in the state's long-term care facilities, especially nursing homes, which account for almost half of COVID-19-related deaths in Illinois. To make them safe and control virus transmission, the government must guarantee these facilities adhere to rigorous mitigation measures: aggressive, repeated testing of residents and workers for infection; heightened environmental cleaning including spraying all high-touch services with disinfectant several times daily; and everyone wearing masks all the time.

If federal and local government reopening proposals are to work, two keys are mitigation and testing. As businesses come back, the public must maintain meticulous attention to infection control. Wearing a mask remains essential when leaving the house, particularly in stores, elevators, public transportation, lobbies and breakrooms — basically any enclosed areas. As workplaces reopen, employees must mask and wash hands frequently. They must take special care in elevators and when opening doors, and if they are sick, stay home. All nonessential business employees should work from home.

But safe reopening requires further measures. The strength of public health is surveillance — testing to find those infected. Once identified, those testing positive should be isolated and close contacts quarantined. It's important to target surveillance in the highest-risk communities. Currently, cases in Chicago occur disproportionately in minority communities, especially in Hispanic and African American neighborhoods. The city should make concerted efforts to test widely in these communities and test as many people as possible, regardless of whether they are exhibiting symptoms. Unfortunately, in large urban areas such as Chicago, contact tracing may be quite difficult.

The Centers for Disease Control and Prevention has authored recommendations for phased-in reopening of churches, mosques and synagogues. These involve restricting attendance to 10 or fewer until it is safe to expand, as well as masking, restricting the sharing of frequently touched objects, maintaining social distancing at services and scrupulous attention to environmental cleaning.

Restaurants and bars that can operate outside during the summer may be able to open, but many will have trouble staying afloat with social distancing rules being applied, because they depend on customer volume to turn a profit. It is a problem without an easy solution.

Schools merit special attention. Children may be less susceptible to the virus and adults in the school setting may pose the greater risk of transmission. The role of children in community spread is still uncertain. The decision on school openings will depend on events this summer but, assuming proper precautions, one approach would be to first open junior high and high schools, where parents are less involved with transporting students to school, before opening classes for smaller children.

The social and economic consequences of our COVID-19 response eventually create their own public health problems. The country will essentially be a laboratory of different experiments in various states and regions; some experiments may fail and provide useful lessons. The optimal strategy will be some middle ground that acknowledges the economy must reopen, slowly, and our efforts will be accompanied by some low-level but unavoidable risk.

This is a tenuous balance with no clear path. Good judgment and wisdom from our scientists and leaders will not be sufficient. Strategies for a carefully planned and phased reopening should be developed collaboratively with the major stakeholders — the public. Remember the admonition of Sgt. Phil Esterhaus from the classic 1980s television police drama "Hill Street Blues" (recommended TV couch fare), who reminded his cops every day, "Let's be careful out there."

Virgin Soil Epidemic – Are We the Aztecs?

Cory Franklin *Chicago Life* 7·1·20

There are, as Shakespeare's Hamlet said, "more things in heaven and earth than are dreamt of in our philosophy". He meant that human knowledge is imperfect and limited, a painful lesson of the COVID-19 pandemic. In the United States, the number of coronavirus cases is soaring and the body counts mount, while we live with the hope that social distancing, testing, and quarantining contacts will ultimately control or at least forestall the contagion. Much of the world including Western Europe, the UK and Israel, are in a similar situation - hoping that some government strategy contains a virus that was underestimated by everyone only a few months ago. Who could foresee a United States increase of more than four million cases and 150,000 deaths in less than six months?

Social distancing is sound epidemiology, but, as Hamlet observed, even it has its limits because COVID-19 is so new and there is much we still don't know. We don't have a good handle on how many people actually have the virus, how people acquired it, or why some people are asymptomatic while others suffer rapidly fatal lung and heart complications. Nor do we know if anyone is immune to it. That is one aspect of the pandemic that has received little attention by the press: not what we do but who we are.

Host immunity is central to understanding all infectious diseases. In some cases, we have developed vaccines that have essentially eliminated some of the scourges of the last century – diphtheria, polio, whooping cough - but in other cases genetics, immunology, nutrition and other factors still determine whether people ultimately acquire infections. To understand how important immunity is, consider the recent measles outbreaks in the United States. Measles is an especially contagious disease, even more so than coronavirus. Those who receive vaccinations are protected, as are those who have had measles in the past, but outbreaks continue to occur in clusters of people who have not been vaccinated and have no immunity. How much of a role does innate immunity play in the COVID-19 pandemic?

Some researchers are now considering whether COVID-19 could be a "virgin soil epidemic", an epidemic in which an at-risk population has not had prior contact with, and consequently lacks immunological defense against, a disease that invades the community. In the history of colonization of the New World during the 15th and 16th centuries, the indigenous populations of North America had no immunity to many of the diseases brought by European settlers. Devastating epidemics were the result.

Do Western Europeans and North Americans lack some measure of immunity to coronavirus the people of East Asia have? The COVID-19 epidemic was controlled in Wuhan (if we are to believe Chinese officials), Singapore, Hong Kong, and South Korea relatively quickly with vigorous isolation. But did innate immunity play a role? In 2003, China was exposed to a related coronavirus, SARS, which mysteriously died out rather suddenly. Did that and other previous exposures to similar coronaviruses and their Asian animal vectors confer some level of immunity in Eastern Asia absent in America and Western Europe? How did huge populations centers like Beijing, Shanghai, and Seoul essentially avoid such a contagious virus while it continues to burn through Florida, California, and Texas (currently more than 1.4 million cases, more than all but two countries in the world)?

The most insightful observation about COVID-19 was made by Dr. Anthony Fauci when he told CNN, "You've got to be realistic, and you've got to understand that you don't make the timeline, the virus makes the timeline." Channeling his inner Hamlet, Dr. Fauci understands what many people don't, namely in times like these, there are some things that are out of our control, no matter what politicians or scientists say. We should continue sound containment strategies and work assiduously on a vaccine, but as we used to say when I worked in the intensive care unit, "We do our best, but Nature always gets the final word."

In the 16th century, despite being vastly outnumbered the Spanish conquistador Cortes conquered the Aztec nation, the most advanced culture in Mesoamerica, what is now Mexico. Cortes was aided by a stealth ally, the smallpox virus, which travelled with the conquistadors from Spain to the New World. The Spaniards, having been exposed to related viruses in Europe, were relatively immune. The Aztecs, with no similar exposure, suffered staggering losses.

Could we be the modern-day Aztecs facing the consequences of a distant virus that has made it to our shores?

Four Lingering Areas of Uncertainty Concerning COVID-19

Cory Franklin Robert A. Weinstein *Inside Sources* 9·14·20

With fall approaching, the devastation from COVID-19 cannot be understated. In the United States, the case total has topped 6 million; the number of deaths will soon pass 200,000. Not to mention the attendant disruption of children's education and the concurrent economic havoc.

This is all a result of a microscopic coronavirus, the agent responsible for COVID-19. Everywhere, the best minds in medicine, epidemiology, public health and virology work assiduously to understand the COVID-19 coronavirus — with tremendous advances. But as any good scientist readily acknowledges, the more we learn, the less we know, because knowledge makes the subject infinitely more complex.

Here are four areas of significant uncertainty despite nearly a year of experience with the coronavirus:

Mode of transmission:

The virus is disseminated two ways: through the air and less commonly through contact with contaminated surfaces. COVID-19 is known to spread primarily by respiratory droplets produced by close talking, sneezing or coughing. These droplets travel up to six feet before drying out or falling to the ground.

Recently, another form of airborne transmission, aerosol, has been proposed by an international group of 239 scientists in the journal Clinical Infectious Diseases. Aerosols, much smaller particles than droplets, emanate from a person's mouth, remain in the air longer and travel greater distances, especially indoors. How common is aerosol spread? Unknown.

But the scientists propose greater measures to prevent this risk by improving indoor ventilation in public buildings, workplaces, schools, hospitals and nursing homes. They advocate supplementing indoor air with clean outdoor air, minimizing recirculation, and employing high-efficiency air filtration and germ-killing ultraviolet lights.

Community immunity:

When a significant percentage of a community becomes immune to a contagious disease, because of previous infection and having been vaccinated, the spread of the disease (e.g. polio or measles) becomes less likely. If a vaccine is available, protection by community immunity depends on the percentage of people vaccinated and the percentage who have already acquired the disease. With no vaccine available, as is currently the case with COVID-19, we are not close to community immunity, which would require a high percentage, perhaps 60 percent to 70 percent of the population to be immune from infection.

Now more than a dozen scientists, in interviews with *The New York Times* published in August, said the threshold is likely to be much lower: just 50 percent, perhaps even less. They speculate that community immunity may be achieved with a lower percentage of people infected — provided that adequate mitigation measures are followed. They do not advocate trying to achieve this as policy, merely as a possible explanation why in some places, like areas of New York City, London and Mumbai, once extremely high infections rates have fallen precipitously.

Vaccines:

Control of most viral infections, especially those formerly the scourge of childhood, depends on development, manufacture and deployment of effective vaccines. A safe COVID-19 vaccine is likely to be crucial for global control of the pandemic. A wide range of COVID-19 vaccine candidates are in various stages of development worldwide; in the United States three are currently in Phase 3 clinical trials (the last step before public release).

The precise safety and effectiveness of these vaccines must be established before emergency use can be authorized, but the process is difficult, especially considering the limited amount of data that can be amassed in a short time. Other unknowns include the extent and durability of immunity the vaccine will confer and of course, what proportion of the public will agree to vaccination.

Reopening schools:

At some point, schools must reopen. School is essential to childhood growth — mental, social and emotional — but there is considerable uncertainty about how much risk is involved with reopening. A related question is how likely are children to transmit the virus to adults in and out of school.

Results to date are unclear — European schools have been reopening but it is too early to tell the extent of their success. Experience with American universities has been disappointing, with clusters of infections reported even before classes begin. Campus partying and alcohol do not lend themselves to a safe environment.

Reopening will require novel approaches. Younger children appear to be more resilient when infected, but while safe, they are not absolutely safe (children are never absolutely safe in terms of communicable diseases). Initial reopenings may be more successful with younger students, perhaps kindergarten through fifth grade.

Rapid saliva tests to facilitate frequent testing may soon become the norm. The University of Illinois currently requires testing twice per week of all faculty, staff and students. It is unconscionable that no one in government has advocated open-environment tent schools in warmer regions and in the north before the weather turns inclement. In the early part of the 20th century, more than 100 cities operated open-air schools, with the intention of preventing tuberculosis.

These are only some areas where there are no definitive answers about COVID-19. Uncertainty exists about which treatments are effective, exactly how the virus spreads through different regions of the country, and the complicated equation of excess deaths which includes delays in treatment of other diseases as well as diseases of despair (subtracting the reduced deaths from events like automobile and vehicular accidents).

The German writer Johann Wolfgang von Goethe once said, "Everything is simpler than you think and more complex than you can imagine." COVID-19 reminds us how true that is.

Four Factors That Lead to Coronavirus Spread

Cory Franklin *Inside Sources* 10·4·20

The United States recently passed the grim benchmarks of 200,000 COVID deaths and 7,000,000 cases — both of which are the highest figures in the world by significant margins, although if current trends continue, India will pass the U.S. in total number of cases sometime this fall.

The dramatic American COVID numbers invite comparisons with other countries — hence, ubiquitous articles by pundits on why can't we be more like South Korea, what we could have learned from Germany, or if we should have managed the pandemic like Sweden (including a recent exchange on the floor of the Senate between Dr. Anthony Fauci and Sen. Rand Paul on whether the U.S. and Sweden can be compared.) These arguments are superficially appealing. However, most people, from senators to epidemiologists to journalists, fail to appreciate that the United States has a unique profile in terms of several basic characteristics that help determine whether or not an outbreak will occur. In truth, the United States is not directly comparable to any single country, and it is difficult to draw firm conclusions about the American response, good or bad, based on what has occurred elsewhere in the world.

Here are four factors that are crucial to the likelihood of COVID spread. They are certainly not the only four factors, nor are they absolutely determinant. There are definitely many other causes, some known, some unknown. And there is some overlap between them — admittedly they are not completely independent variables. But each of these matters in its own way in terms of viral spread.

Population: Basically more people, more potential hosts for the virus, more possible cases. The U.S. has the third highest population in the world. Of the eight countries with the most COVID cases, five are among the top 10 most populous countries in the world (U.S., India, Brazil, Russia and Mexico, and that doesn't include China because we may not be able to trust their real COVID figures). In the U.S., population matters as well — seven of the top 10 most populous states are among the top ten in COVID cases (California, Texas, Florida, New York, Illinois, Georgia, North Carolina).

Size of the country: COVID is basically a regional disease. As such, it is harder to eradicate viral spread nationwide in a larger country because new outbreaks can come from anywhere. The US is fourth in the world in land mass. Five of the world's top ten countries by area are also in the top ten by COVID cases (US, India, Brazil, Russia and Argentina).

Mobility: The more people travel, the more likely the spread of the virus. Mobility is hard to measure directly, but according to *The Washington Post*, the U.S. is the number one country in the world in terms of domestic mobility and travel. (At the outbreak of the pandemic, the U.S. was also third in receiving international tourists, just behind France and Spain, two of the most heavily affected countries by COVID in the world).

Diversity: There is unquestionably a genetic component to viral spread. A more diverse country will have a greater chance that some of its population will demonstrate resistance to infection, and there will also be a greater number of susceptible people with less immunity. Like mobility, diversity can be difficult to measure, but according to the Pew Research Center, the U.S. is more diverse than most Western European or Asian countries but less diverse than Canada, Brazil, Mexico or most African countries.

In summary, the United States is at or near the top of the world in population, area, and mobility, and more diverse than most industrialized countries. No other country has a similar profile. The country that is closest to the United States is Brazil: fifth in area, seventh in population, more diverse but less mobile. Brazil, not coincidentally, has over four million COVID cases, the third largest number in the world, and virtually the same per capita case and death totals as the United States. Canada, which is frequently compared to the U.S., has a far smaller number of COVID cases. But Canada is ranked 39th in the world by population and while it has a greater area than the U.S., 80-85 percent of its population lives within 100 miles of the U.S. border; the vast majority of the Canadian land mass is either uninhabited or sparsely populated so containment of the virus is easier.

None of this is meant as either a defense or a criticism of the current administration and its COVID advisers. For those who want to see Donald Trump lose the coming election, the case and death numbers, with the U.S. as the world leader, provide a convenient opportunity to make the claim he has done an especially egregious job of handling the pandemic.

But just as Newton's Third Law of Motion predicts, for every action there is an equal and opposite reaction — in this case by Trump's defenders who point out limitations in these numbers. All in all, this amounts to an unresolvable argument, basically a political food fight worthy of the cafeteria in the movie *Animal House*.

A COVID Vaccine: The End of the Beginning

Cory Franklin Robert A. Weinstein *Inside Sources* 11·16·20

The greatest medical achievement of the 18th century was the introduction of the smallpox vaccination. In an era when medicine was primitive, smallpox was responsible for hundreds of thousands of deaths in Europe and the Americas. The great English physician Edward Jenner discovered that scratching a patient's skin with fluid from relatively innocuous cowpox blisters could safely prevent a related but more serious disease, smallpox. This was the birth of the vaccine. Now we are on the verge of a similarly great medical achievement of the 21st century — the COVID vaccine.

The early trial results of a vaccine developed by Pfizer in partnership with BioNTech are encouraging — 90 percent of vaccine recipients were protected from becoming ill with COVID-19, with no reports of serious toxicity. Many details, especially how long it will protect a recipient, still need review but 90 percent is in the range of the successful vaccines that have controlled a number of childhood diseases. Many details must be worked out including cost, supply and distribution.

The Pfizer vaccine currently requires two injections, and there is a limited amount of vaccine accessible.

Because the drug relies on a live segment of RNA, to avoid destruction of the genetic material, it must be kept at extremely cold temperatures, not generally available in your physician's office. This is the first time a vaccine has been successfully created by deploying genetic code into cells, another important unknown. Companies besides Pfizer are moving ahead with different vaccines that may eventually be better and more practical. The UK is preparing to roll out the Oxford vaccine, developed by AstraZeneca, which is cheaper, more durable and easier to administer than the Pfizer vaccine. The early UK experience bears scrutiny.

We are currently in the steep uphill curve of the third and most dangerous wave of COVID-19, with more people hospitalized than at any time during the pandemic. Right now, Illinois has the highest 10-day average of new cases of any state in the country — nearly 10,000 new cases daily. Nationally, there are now more than 11 million total COVID cases and 250,000 deaths. Fortunately, mortality continues to drop (rising death totals are a function of rising cases) and there are currently several treatments in use, the combination of which likely saved the life of President Trump.

Test-tube engineered "monoclonal" antibodies — so-called because they come from a single cell type and target a specific site on the virus — have just been approved for general use in high-risk patients. Their best use is to forestall worsening infection in outpatients and prevent hospitalization. The anti-viral drug remdesivir can shorten hospital stay. Finally, new techniques to administer oxygen along with the steroid dexamethasone have decreased mortality in ICU patients.

But prevention remains the preferred option over treatment. The role of vaccines in terms of public health cannot be overstated; they have saved far more lives than antibiotics. As late as the 1960s, two million people died worldwide from smallpox, but by 1980 when the vaccine was delivered strategically throughout the Third World, the disease was eradicated. (The two-century lag between the first smallpox vaccine and the eradication of the disease was because of the difficulty of distribution to remote areas.)

Measles, mumps, chickenpox, polio, whooping cough and other childhood scourges have all caused terrible morbidity or mortality at some time. They have been largely eliminated by industry's ability to develop effective and safe vaccines, administered by a well-supported, trustworthy public health and medical infrastructure. Public acceptance of a vaccine is essential.

Some people balk at vaccines and childhood vaccination rates have not been universal even in affluent areas. But they have been sufficient to contain once dreadful diseases at extremely low levels. In situations where the public has turned away from effective vaccines, children have suffered unnecessarily. Measles was declared eliminated in the United States in 2000, but in 2019 there were over 1000 cases due to unvaccinated children, primarily the result of parental reluctance about vaccination. Political leadership must play a role.

When Dr. Jenner developed the smallpox vaccine, he received immediate support throughout Europe. Napoleon, the most powerful man in the world, had the entire French army vaccinated. Although Britain and France were at war, Napoleon awarded Jenner, a British citizen, a medal and freed two British prisoners at his request, such was the importance of Jenner's discovery.

The winter months will be very difficult with the prospect of huge numbers of community-acquired infection and overloaded hospitals. Mitigation, including masking and social distancing, remains essential and even more important during this time of massive community spread of infection. These mitigation measures also provide value-added protection from flu, colds and other respiratory viruses. Widespread masking is a small concession for phased increases of in-person schooling and fewer restrictions on a variety of businesses, industries and sports. It is certainly preferable to tight lockdown. Does a vaccine mean we are close to stopping the pandemic?

Not in the short run. But the critical message is that a viable vaccine can be developed. As Winston Churchill told Parliament after the first successful defeat of the German army in World War II after the North African campaign, "This is not the end. This is not even the beginning of the end. But it is perhaps the end of the beginning."

Public Health Officials Must Regain The Public's Trust

Cory Franklin *Inside Sources* 12·2·20

As the winter phase of the COVID pandemic approaches, there has been a reshuffling of the cards: Several vaccines will be available shortly to the public, more quickly than anticipated. Currently, it is not clear which vaccine will prove superior based on cost, availability and effectiveness, but no matter how effective and safe they are, public support for, and acceptance of them, is essential.

This is a critical area where our health officials must roll up their sleeves and improve their efforts to communicate with the public. So far, the communication record of the public health officials in the pandemic has garnered a generous gentleman's C — at best. Last winter, most minimized the threat the virus posed, initially to avoid panic and out of fear of xenophobia. Then came an immediate shift into DEFCON 1, essentially sowing confusion on what the actual risk of COVID was.

From there came the backtrack on masks: first of no benefit, then beneficial but to be rationed carefully, and eventually full-mask advocacy with an especial fervor. The common-sense message of social distancing was also compromised when physicians were more than willing to suspend distancing in the name of political causes. Either large crowds risk viral spread or they do not, independent of social justice. People pick up on these kinds of things.

Perhaps the most damaging blow to the public trust was the failure of the public health community to anticipate and communicate the social, economic and *public health aftermath* of a lockdown. Testifying before Congress in May, Dr. Anthony Fauci acknowledged his lack of expertise in matters economic — not that he should be expected to be an expert in such matters — but it suggested a disinclination on his part and that of his professional colleagues to acknowledge the damage of the unintended consequences of closing down large segments of society.

The net effect of all this hurly-burly is that officials have put any claim they have to public trust in jeopardy. And trust is paramount. With a vaccine rollout, the public health community must refine their approach to addressing the concerns and questions of their intended audience — patients, politicians and the citizenry. A banal bromide like "trust the science" helps neither science nor the public in the long run.

The key is effective communication: neither proselytizing nor bland recitation of the facts. So here are some keys to informing the public and helping people make informed decisions about COVID vaccinations:

— State the benefits and risks with the knowledge that the information is necessarily incomplete. This should be done in a way that people can understand and allows them to make reasonable comparisons.

— Don't pretend to know more than you do. There is plenty we do not know about these new vaccines. Tell the public that. Reassure them that you are making every effort to stay abreast of every development and will inform them of your findings – and don't cherry-pick data. Cherry-picking data — selecting one example to prove a point while ignoring a counterexample — is a form of intellectual dishonesty.

Scientists have a tendency to be patronizing about things the public does not understand. Resist that tendency. People will harbor misconceptions; be alert to addressing them. Explain, not in an authoritative or dismissive way, why the public may be mistaken in its beliefs. The facts may change and your opinion might change as well. Say why you changed your mind. Every time you go before the public, remember what you've said before. Nothing undermines credibility more than contradicting your prior remarks.

Be prepared for the unexpected. Don't pretend you knew it was coming. A classic example was in 1976 when, based on the advice of his public health experts, President Ford created a plan to vaccinate every man, woman and child in the United States for the swine flu. The flu barely materialized, but hundreds of vaccinated patients developed an elevated risk for the serious neurologic condition, Guillain-Barre syndrome.

What the medical profession tells the public, and how it tells them, is not only important in the context of a COVID vaccine. It is also important for what is left to future generations. We will eventually recover from COVID but this is not our last public health crisis. One of the most important things doctors can do is develop better principles of communication and refine them to minimize future health threats. Will the public line up for a vaccine? The Old Testament advises, "The Lord hath created medicines out of the earth; and he that is wise will not abhor them."

The ancient wisdom of that one sentence is the message our public health people must impart effectively.

A Year's Experience With COVID-19

Cory Franklin Robert A. Weinstein *Inside Sources* 1·20·21

The first documented case of COVID-19 infection in the United States occurred on January 20, 2020 (there is strong evidence of undetected cases in prior months). That means the country has now had one year of experience with the virus that has caused the worst pandemic since the Spanish flu 100 years ago. While we still don't understand many things about COVID-19, in the past year we have acquired valuable knowledge about viral transmission, COVID testing, management of the critically ill, and keeping schools open. We also have vaccines – a pipedream a year ago. Here are some things we know today that we did not know when the first patient presented to a hospital in Washington state last January.

It was originally believed that people caught the virus by touching contaminated surfaces and through particle droplets transmitted through speaking, coughing and singing. Now we realize, that besides those two mechanisms inhalation of smaller particles – aerosols – are an opportunistic form of transmission, a potential problem in overcrowded spaces with poor ventilation. Masks confer a good level of protection but are not an absolute defense; handwashing and social distancing remain important adjuncts to masks. This is especially true with new virus strains that may be more contagious. Every pullback of mitigation effort when case numbers fell has been followed by epidemic resurgence.

The current status of COVID testing is far more sophisticated than a year ago, with different tests for different situations. The best test for diagnosing symptomatic patients is different from one identifying potential asymptomatic carriers who might transmit the virus. To diagnose a patient who has symptoms, a PCR assay on a nasal swab is the most practical and effective test.

To ascertain who may be actively contagious, e.g., for those concerned before family gatherings or travel, the rapid antigen test from saliva or nasal swab can detect high loads of virus in respiratory secretions. This test, although not as reliable as the gold-standard PCR test, can be performed anywhere, is inexpensive, does not require expensive equipment or special training, and provides results in under an hour. Speed and the ability to re-test generally outweigh reduced accuracy in these situations. Positive results with the rapid antigen test should be verified with the more accurate PCR-based test. Soon, even simpler tests will be available to the public along the lines of the home pregnancy testing. Finally, there are blood antibody tests for those who want to know if they have been previously infected.

In the early phase of the pandemic, thousands of people died because they were placed on ventilators to support their virus-damaged lungs. We have discovered that the virus causes different types of lung damage. In certain patients, ventilators increase that damage. In these cases when oxygen levels become low, patients are better treated by being placed in a prone position – on the stomach – and receiving high levels of oxygen by nasal cannula. This does not work for everyone and there are still many patients who can and should be treated with ventilators (contrary to some press reports). Just not all patients.

In addition, there are currently at least three therapeutics available. Dexamethasone and remdesivir are available for hospitalized patients. For mildly symptomatic outpatients, monoclonal antibodies are effective (and are underused).

Owing to fear of COVID transmission, many schools closed early in the pandemic. But CDC data show that children in schools have a lower risk of being infected with COVID-19 than those not attending school. Moreover, children are probably less likely to transmit the virus than adults are. Children, especially younger children, need in-person learning, social contacts, meals that schools provide, and the support structure teachers create. Many schools have opened without incident, and reopening of schools must be a top priority, even before the whole country is vaccinated. Besides adequate numbers of masks, and plenty of surface sanitizers and hand soaps, schools should have ample supplies of rapid antigen testing materials to ascertain who might be contagious, along with special areas (trailers or tents) to conduct testing. Reopening of schools may require changes in school routines: teachers rather than children moving between rooms for classes; staggered class times to minimize crowded hallways; and reconfiguration of hallways, classrooms and cafeterias to maximize personal separation. Windows should remain open when possible. Fans should be used to increase air circulation. In general, the need for special ventilation has proved unnecessary.

Hospitals have learned that if feasible, COVID patients should be separated from non-COVID patients. Current infection control strategies and activities allow many hospitals to continue the necessary care of non-COVID patients, including elective surgery and other essential diagnostic and therapeutic care.

One year ago, we didn't have a vaccine against COVID. Now, we have two, with several others in the pipeline. The best vaccine is the one that you take. But vaccination of our entire country will take several months.

Deployment of vaccines needs an urgent overhaul, with the goal of vaccinating as many as possible, as quickly as possible, starting with the most fragile and at-risk individuals. During this ramp up, we must continue our mitigation strategies—face masks, social distancing, and hand hygiene. The more people vaccinated and the better our mitigation efforts, the sooner all of society can reopen and put the nightmare of 2020 behind us.

COVID-19 vaccines are a must in health care facilities as delta variant remains at large

Cory Franklin Robert A. Weinstein *Chicago Tribune*
1·28·21

In the latest phase of the COVID-19 pandemic, the extremely contagious delta variant is now causing at least 80% of the infections in the U.S. The emergence of the delta variant has dispelled any optimistic notion that the vaccine rollout would provide a rapid end to the pandemic. Put simply, zero-COVID-19 is not a realistic goal in the United States anytime soon.

With infections in the fourth wave now exceeding 60,000 per day on some days, we are drawing down on our arsenal to fight the virus. As an adjunct to the vaccines, we need better, cheaper and more accurate rapid testing for the virus so we can more effectively manage the situation in schools, the workplace and social venues.

In addition, the search must continue for new treatments, including oral medications, to treat early infection (our best treatment currently is the underused monoclonal antibodies that are administered intravenously). Until improved testing and greater treatment options are available, we must work with what we have to minimize the harm. Minimizing harm begins with the health care workplace.

As things stand now, visiting the hospital or clinic can be a harrowing experience if you have a weakened immune system -- or even if you don't. The high level of protection conferred by vaccination makes it indisputably essential for those with close and continuing contact with patients. To avoid spread of infection -- especially to young people, the unvaccinated and those with weakened immune systems -- vaccination should be mandatory for anyone who works in a hospital, clinic or long-term care facility. This has to include everyone from the top executives in their suites to the front-line environmental services people working the night shift.

Consider the elderly man recently diagnosed with cancer who must ride on a crowded elevator to reach the oncology clinic for his chemotherapy treatments. Then he must move to a small examining room barely large enough for him, the doctor, nurse and a trainee, any of whom may or may not be vaccinated. (The best estimates are that as many as 30% of all Chicago-area hospital and health systems employees remain unvaccinated.) For those caring for our most vulnerable patients in hospitals, clinics and nursing homes, vaccination should be mandated by the respective institutions. If the health care community does not lead by example to protect those patients and others like them, then who will? There are many well-documented examples of spread of COVID-19 from health care workers to patients, between health care workers, and from patients to staff. In some cases, this has resulted in serious illness. There is general agreement among infectious disease experts, medical ethicists and public health authorities on the need for mandatory vaccination in health care settings, and a mandatory vaccine policy for health care facilities has support in the law.

In June, a federal district court in Texas rejected an attempt by Houston medical workers to challenge the legality of their employer's decision to require that all employees receive a COVID-19 vaccine. According to the National Law Review, as part of its reasoning, the court explained that the vaccine mandate is part of the bargain of at-will employment and does not constitute coercion, since the hospital is simply "trying to do their business of saving lives without giving (employees) the COVID-19 virus. It is a choice made to keep staff, patients and their families safer. ... Every employment includes limits on the worker's behavior in exchange for his remuneration. This is all part of the bargain."

We are fighting an implacable foe in COVID-19 and more so in the delta variant. Some politicians and health care experts used to speak of "crushing COVID." In retrospect, that was wishful thinking -- there is no quick exit strategy. It is impossible to say how long the virus will be with us in all its protean manifestations, but it will not disappear anytime soon.

We must learn to live with COVID-19, while at the same time doing everything we can, scientifically and socially, to suppress it. Along those lines, requiring health care facilities to mandate vaccination for all employees is one small step in the larger battle against COVID-19, a battle that might go on for months -- or years.

Got 'vaccine clout'? Most of us don't, and so we feel like powerless losers

Cory Franklin *Chicago Tribune* 2·2·21

"What is vaccine clout?" A term popularized in Chicago, "clout" was defined by legendary newspaper columnist Mike Royko as political influence exercised through patronage, fixing, money, favors or similar measures. Clout is essentially power exercised with the intent of circumventing rules — bending or breaking them for personal benefit.

With the recent development of vaccines for the ubiquitous COVID-19 comes a new phenomenon: vaccine clout. Distribution of the vaccine has been shambolic to say the least and has people, ranging from the rich and famous to the plebe who simply has the right connections, finding creative ways to get the vaccine before those who would benefit more. Examples abound.

In Florida, a West Palm Beach senior living center made vaccines available to wealthy board members, even though the vaccines had been intended for residents and staff. Likewise, a New Jersey hospital administered vaccines to well-heeled donors and relatives of executives before making it available to the general public. In the first days of vaccine distribution, the young-adult children of the hospital officials got the vaccine at a time when New

Jersey vaccine recipients were less than 5% minority and only a third of the supply had gone to those over 65.

The inability to get the vaccine is sending regular people, frustrated by frozen websites and closed appointment windows, looking for connections as well — maybe a church member, a business associate or a golfing buddy. Facebook groups are forming to share connections. Anybody who might have access.

How did it come to this? There is more than enough blame to go around. Armed with guidelines from public health officials, hospitals received priority in obtaining vaccine. The experience in New Jersey was not unique — too often hospitals prioritized hospital bureaucrats with little or no patient contact at the expense of the communities they are supposed to serve.

At Stanford Hospital, there was palpable outrage when administrators and other employees working from home got priority over almost all of Stanford's 1,300 medical residents. Before a correction was made, Stanford officials blamed the mess on a faulty artificial intelligence algorithm. Which tells you two things: first, imagine what lies ahead when humans put their blind trust in artificial intelligence algorithms and, second, clout generally has a good backup story when it is exposed. This one just happens to have the distinction of being a 21st century excuse. A good deal of culpability lies with the politicians overseeing the public health agencies. Some of these politicians spent a great deal of time in front of television cameras bragging about their handling of the COVID-19 crisis (they know who they are) and overpromising the number of people that could be vaccinated quickly. These same politicians wound up underdelivering, and woefully so.

How did this come about? Mountains of red tape, lack of cooperation at the city/county/state/federal levels, not enough teamwork between the private and public sectors and, finally, overly rigid adherence to guidelines for which the public health officials must share the blame. The Centers for Disease Control and Prevention has belatedly acknowledged, at least indirectly, how their guidelines detailing who can get the vaccine and how long to wait between shots have contributed to the problem. A spokesman for the agency was quoted in *the Washington Post*, "We received feedback that some flexibility in our language might be helpful to reduce barriers to vaccination ... as always, CDC encourages people to follow our guidance around intervals and interchangeability, but we also don't want our guidance to be so rigid that it creates unintended barriers." Bureaucratic speak for "we went overboard with the guidelines."

Political incompetence and rigid adherence to arbitrary rules are the fertile soil that permits clout to grow. As Royko described, the purpose of clout is to bend or break the rules. So, there is little surprise that clout has evolved in the world of COVID-19 vaccination. Being vaccinated is essentially a valuable commodity, and any valuable commodity will be sought after and bartered for. (It's a wonder there aren't more reports of black marketing and counterfeiting vaccine — the illegal dark side of clout.)

The most important thing to know about any kind of clout is that it builds resentment for those who benefit from it. But in this case, vaccine clout is different from a do-nothing job or a trash-hauling contract, where the general public loses very little directly. This type of clout leaves people feeling like powerless losers, at risk for death.

In that respect, vaccine clout is the worst type of clout.

The COVID Crossroads

Cory Franklin Robert A. Weinstein *Inside Sources* 2·24·21

The winter of our COVID discontent is upon us. The
U.S. has suffered over 28 million cases and 500,000 deaths
during the pandemic year. But now we are at a crossroads,
with the situation on the ground currently at odds with the
one in the air, both metaphorically and literally.

Many virologists and epidemiology experts forecast,
with some confidence, that the next few weeks will see the
worst of the pandemic, primarily the result of new viral
mutants, more contagious and possibly more lethal. These
new strains are appearing with greater prevalence in
several states. Experts predict we are in for the long haul
with COVID, and these pessimistic forecasts have
prompted the Biden administration to consider tighter
restrictions on domestic flights and businesses. But there is
another angle to the situation.

Running counter to those dire expert predictions
are the current downward trends in the overall viral
spread, which have been considerable (and underplayed in
the news media). In the U.S. in the past month, COVID
cases have dropped by an average of 150,000 per day,
more than 60 percent. Hospitalizations have decreased by
nearly 50 percent and intensive care cases and ventilator
use have also dropped steadily since mid-January. While

deaths have not fallen off as drastically as COVID cases –
there is a 14-28 day lag between the two–they have begun a
downtrend. With the drop in cases, deaths will almost
certainly fall further, perhaps dramatically in the next
month.

This is unquestionably good news, and it comes in
conjunction with greater attention to vaccine rollout by the
Biden administration. Vaccination rates are increasing,
and the U.S. is currently second only to Israel in the
percentage of the population completely vaccinated (albeit
a distant second). Along with the plummeting cases and
continued mitigation efforts, a plan designed to maximize
the number of people vaccinated in the shortest time is the
best strategy to suppress mutants – no transmission means
no viral multiplication means no mutants and no fourth
surge.

In this respect, with several suppliers making more
vaccines available, the question of who goes first in a
situation of limited supply takes a backseat to maximizing
the numbers vaccinated. The current tier system
represents guidelines, not rigid mandates, and it would be
a mistake to wait for the completion of one tier before
moving to the next. We must move through the tiers as
quickly as vaccine supplies allow, with the realization that
the last 20-30 percent of each tier could take 70-80
percent of our effort. So, we should proceed with the most

fragile and at-risk populations and move quickly to the next tiers, with the goal of vaccinating as many as possible, as quickly as possible. In this instance, that is the surest way to achieve health care equity.

The public should be aware that current conditions suggest that even at high vaccination rates, the well-publicized target of herd immunity might not be achievable. Complete herd immunity may be unlikely because of vaccine hesitancy, the limits of vaccine effectiveness, and future mutant strains that may not respond to the vaccine. This is not a reason for pessimism, nor is it a reason to forgo vaccination. It presents a strong case to continue near-term mitigation efforts, especially social distancing and masking.

Our goal for vaccines – and it is certainly achievable – should be to curtail viral spread to the greatest degree possible and prevent severe illness in those who contract the virus. In that respect, besides vaccination, we must continue to develop new treatments for COVID and deploy the ones we have more effectively including, for newly infected at-risk outpatients, monoclonal antibodies, a drastically underused therapy throughout the pandemic.

Does the possibility of not reaching herd immunity mean the coronavirus will never go away as some experts fear? Possibly, but no one can say for certain. Like other microbes, it will do what it is going to do. But we should be confident we can develop the resources and muster the will to manage the pandemic and re-establish normality.

In this vein, the essential reopening of our schools deserves special mention. Returning to in-person instruction is well supported by science, epidemiology, and the experience of school systems globally. The real risk for teachers and students is not in properly managed schools; it is in the activities pursued outside of school.

In a moving scene in the Charles Dickens classic, "A Christmas Carol," Ebenezer Scrooge cowers in front of the Spirit of the Future in the graveyard and raises the question of whether the future is preordained, "Are these the shadows of the things that Will be, or are they shadows of things that May be, only?...men's courses will foreshadow certain ends, to which, if persevered in, they must lead, But if the courses be departed from, the ends will change."

The optimist in us hopes that the experts have overestimated the impact of the coronavirus variants. There is certainly a chance, worth hoping for, that the combination of vaccination, mitigation efforts, and virus burnout will permit us to return to normal lives as early as the summer. But as someone observed, we will not be done with the virus until the virus is done with us.

What's Missing in COVID Conversations? Trust

Cory Franklin *Inside Sources* 4·19·21

Has the public lost faith in public health officials, who continue to communicate with so much confusion and ambiguity? During the COVID pandemic, when trust should be the coin of the realm, physicians, researchers, and bureaucrats in the public health community seem unwilling or unable to articulate their message clearly and concisely. Because COVID presents a unique set of problems and continuously evolving circumstances, it is especially important to avoid certain pitfalls when talking to the public.

The most important of these priorities is "thou shalt not mislead the public." It does not surprise us when politicians lie, but we don't expect mendacity from our doctors – nor should we. Case in point: Dr. Anthony Fauci, the country's recognized COVID authority. In a December 24 interview with *The New York Times,* Fauci admitted he deliberately understated the figures needed for herd immunity, partly based on new science but also on his sense the country was not prepared to hear his true feelings.

No matter his paternalistic good intentions, this was a lie. It cost him the trust of many, particularly in light of his statements early in the pandemic about masks being unnecessary: "Right now in the United States, people should not be walking around with masks." In his defense, his comment about masks preceded research that pronounced masks somewhat effective. But when experts shade the truth or project unwarranted certainty, they risk having subsequent discoveries undermine their credibility.

A related pitfall public health experts should have avoided: appearing to be inflexible know-it-alls even as situations evolved. Consistency is a virtue, dogmatism is not. Everybody has been wrong about COVID (I predicted we would be through the pandemic last summer), and it behooves us to admit our mistakes, rather than cling to them. This recalls a famous quote attributed variously to among others, John Maynard Keynes, Winston Churchill, and Paul Samuelson, "When events change, I change my mind. What do you do?" Be consistent, but not inflexible.

All of us have heard more than a year's worth of predictions about the future course of the pandemic. Some experts engage freely in these projections, without allowing for uncertainty. They predict surges or huge waves of cases that never occur and then those prognostications are quickly forgotten. This is the medical equivalent of the economists who have successfully predicted "nine of the last five" recessions. A term exists for any COVID prediction that projects out more than six weeks – it's called a "guess."

Another lesson not easily learned is don't overextend expertise. During the first wave of the pandemic, epidemiologists, virologists, and experts such as oncologist Ezekiel Emanuel, strongly advised tight lockdowns without realizing the substantial social and economic costs, which themselves had terrible health consequences, especially for schoolchildren who've been isolated for more than a year. Lockdowns have a place in controlling viral spread in certain situations for a limited time. But imposing them requires the input of experts other than just physicians, who are rarely experts in matters financial or social. Dr. Fauci admitted as much after the fact in a congressional hearing. Venture out of your lane – and don't be surprised if you crash into a wall.

Finally, while personal bias is inevitable, scientific opinions should not be compromised by political concerns. One important goal of science is to minimize personal bias in the search for objective truths. When experts become political, they quickly undermine the very thing they seek to advance. In the case of COVID, a large outdoor gathering carries the risk of becoming a superspreader event whether it is a Black Lives Matter protest or a Sturgis motorcycle rally. When public health experts ignore their own warnings and approve of one but not the other based on their politics, it is obvious they are betraying the very scientific rigor they claim to represent. Why should anyone trust their subsequent statements, policy recommendations, and public mandates? Politicized science is invariably a recipe for the erosion of public trust.

Finally, like their military counterparts, public health officials have an unfortunate tendency "to fight the last war", with a reluctance to learn from history. A prime example was in 1976, when public health officials predicted that a new strain of swine flu would cause a pandemic in the United States. A mass immunization campaign for the country was recommended to President Gerald Ford, which he attempted to implement in good faith. The pandemic never materialized but the vaccine was associated with severe neurologic reactions in several hundred patients.

Two years after the swine flu debacle, President Jimmy Carter's Secretary of Health, Education and Welfare commissioned a report by two prominent scientific policy analysts on the entire episode with special attention devoted to the role of the public health officials in charge of the campaign. The analysts found in the public health response: "overconfidence by specialists in theories spun from meager evidence; conviction fueled by a conjunction of some preexisting agendas; zeal by health professionals to make their superiors do right; premature commitment to deciding more than had to be decided; failure to address uncertainties in such a way as to prepare for reconsideration; insufficient questioning of scientific logic and of implementation prospects; and insensitivity to media relations and the long-term credibility of institutions."

Sound familiar?

The Variant Pandemic: Preparing for Future COVID

Cory Franklin Robert A. Weinstein *Inside Sources* 5·14·21

"In the environment, every victory is temporary, every defeat is permanent." That quote, commonly attributed to Thomas Jefferson, aptly describes our current struggle with COVID-19. After more than a year's worth of death and tragedy, America finally has the upper hand on COVID, thanks to vaccination and mitigation measures. But the virus is a relentless foe; we are still experiencing 50,000 cases a day, while cases and deaths surge in India and rise steadily throughout South America and Southeast Asia.

We must rethink the entire situation because it is now a "variant virus" pandemic. While vaccination may permit us to return to "normal", we may still experience low-level seasonal waves of COVID infection or small regional disease breakouts caused by evolving variants indefinitely. Even now, as we successfully suppress COVID-19, we should prepare for coronavirus infections in coming years, e.g. COVID-22 or COVID-24.

That will require a rededicated scientific effort on a number of fronts. This includes the development of a universal coronavirus vaccine, effective against all variants - something that is harder to achieve than it sounds. To date, we have been unable to come up with a universal vaccine for influenza because the flu virus variants continue to emerge; nature remains stubbornly one step ahead of us. Along with this, we need effective, inexpensive medications to treat the COVID infection itself. Our current drugs to treat COVID-19 are only partially effective and work only in certain situations. What is necessary is a drug, or drugs, on the order of penicillin and the succeeding generations of antibiotics, which have saved millions of lives not by eradicating but by treating antibacterial diseases. Tuberculosis is an example of a disease that annually affects millions worldwide that has been tamed, but unfortunately not eliminated, by effective drug treatment.

As part of the evaluation of new drugs and vaccines, our scientific community should create a more flexible system for assessing and publishing research in the time of a pandemic. COVID-19 illustrated the Scylla and Charybdis of making research public in a timely fashion. Traditional journals often take months to publish important medical findings – an impractical gap when urgent help is needed. The only current alternative is a direct online posting of unreviewed research, which can lead to the proliferation of unvetted opinions and spurious research. In the face of a rapidly evolving situation, where people are dying on a daily basis, there must be a middle ground to disseminate reliable information expeditiously.

In the surveillance mode, we need better systems to identify viral variants. It took the United States the better part of a year to gear up to recognize coronavirus mutations that cause variants to spread in different parts of the country. We will need a distant early warning system to detect mutations that could escape vaccine control and cause future outbreaks. All pandemics are at once local and global, and global control is essential to local control. A brushfire somewhere in the world can become a conflagration everywhere. So, the United States must be part of a redoubled effort to track coronavirus activity in every part of the world.

Locally, there should be a greater push for affordable, rapid, easy point-of-care saliva testing. Think of this type of testing like at-home pregnancy kits, in the sense they are not completely reliable, but accurate enough to prompt further action like seeing your doctor. Convenient point-of-care saliva testing will permit decision-making in minutes about isolation and contact tracing. Such a system would be invaluable in schools, places of employment, airports, and entertainment venues.

Finally, the country should undertake a long-term project to evaluate the quality of ventilation in all public buildings with the intent of minimizing the chances of indoor airborne pathogen spread in the future. Along with this should come greater attention to the actual risk of the ventilation systems of airline cabins. That risk is believed to be extremely low but will require further study.

The coronavirus is an implacable enemy. It has caused nearly 600,000 deaths and untold suffering in the United States, even as it continues to ravage the rest of the world. Absent some remarkable unexpected development, "zero COVID" – the complete eradication of the pathogenic coronavirus – will not be a reality anywhere in the world, including the United States, any time soon. That's why, even in the face of our current successes, we must prepare for a protracted campaign.

Alert, alive.

Beyond Hitchcock: The COVID Origin Story

Cory Franklin *Inside Sources* 6·3·21

How and where did the COVID coronavirus originate? Not even Alfred Hitchcock could devise such an international medical mystery, replete with political implications, foreign intrigue, and diplomatic wrangling. But this is real life, not a whodunnit. Today, a year and a half since the pandemic began, nothing is certain and we don't know who to trust.

The story begins in December 2019 in Wuhan, China, a city of 11 million people. The Communist Chinese Party (CCP) reported to the world the appearance in Wuhan of the first cases of what turned out to be COVID. Since then, the CCP has engaged in misdirection, obfuscation, outright lying, and evidence destruction (early virus samples were destroyed for "biosafety reasons"). Even the original timeline is in doubt after *The Wall Street Journal* reported the hospitalization, prior to December, of three staff members of the Wuhan Institute of Virology (WIV), the laboratory where Chinese scientists were studying the virus.

By mid-January 2020, COVID had spread internationally, although few outside of China appreciated the enormity of the situation. (The CCP locked down Wuhan in late January. Whether they allowed travelers to leave the city and disseminate the virus remains uncertain.)

Questions of the virus's origin began circulating. While some in the U.S., including polarizing figures Sen. Tom Cotton and President Donald Trump, asserted the virus leaked from the WIV laboratory, most scientists and the international press were adamant it did not come from the laboratory but evolved naturally from bats to man through an intermediate animal host. The CCP insisted that the virus first appeared at a Wuhan open wet market. Until recently, this was the conventional wisdom in the lay press and medical literature. To assert otherwise was to engage in conspiracy theory, xenophobia, and perhaps worst of all, validation of Trump.

But science demands an open mind; theories must be fit to the facts, not facts retrofitted to theories. And as John Adams said, "facts are stubborn things." The virus was never isolated at a wet market; that was a lie. An animal intermediate vector, which would basically put to rest the lab leak theory, has never been identified. Without proof of an animal vector, the lab theory remains viable. Moreover, to believe that the virus originated several miles from one of the world's most sophisticated virus labs, with the lab having no role, strains credulity. It would be like discovering a source of radioactivity and denying any connection to a nearby nuclear power plant. That remarkable coincidence will not disappear easily.

In the Bulletin of Atomic Scientists last week, former *New York Times* science editor Nicholas Wade laid out the case for the lab leak theory. It was quickly supported by prominent scientists including Nobel laureate virologist David Baltimore. The script is flipping. Viable hypotheses include natural evolution from an animal vector, an accidental lab leak of a natural virus or an engineered virus; and a deliberate leak of an engineered virus (while less likely, this would amount to biowarfare). Any of these is possible. We still have no conclusive answers.

A good whodunnit requires a cast of characters. We obviously cannot trust the CCP. How about Glenn Kessler, chief writer for the Fact Checker column of *The Washington Post*? In May 2020 he tweeted, "(it is) virtually impossible for the virus to jump from the lab. (With) many interviews with actual scientists... we deal in facts." Now, one year later, he wrote a story headlined, "How the Wuhan Lab-leak Suddenly Became Credible." But it wasn't suddenly; it was always credible.

The World Health Organization? Their ties with China are incestuous. In a joint report in February they declared, "The findings suggest the laboratory incident hypothesis is extremely unlikely to explain introduction of the virus into the human population." Two days later the WHO Secretary-General backtracked, "Some questions have been raised as to whether some hypotheses have been discarded ... I want to clarify that all hypotheses remain open and require further study."

Dr. Anthony Fauci has vacillated on the source of the virus from animal origin to lab leak. He owes the world a frank explanation of all he knows about virus research at the WIV. It is not a crime to be wrong about a hypothesis. The scientific process involves correcting errors and revising hypotheses. But "following the science" means not trying to fool people. One of the greatest scientific minds of our era, Nobel laureate Richard Feynman, once said, "You must not fool yourself, and you are the easiest person to fool."

COVID: What Just Ain't So

Cory Franklin *Inside Sources* 6·21·21

In 1984, a young Australian doctor drank a flask of liquid teeming with bacteria obtained from a patient suffering from indigestion. The doctor thus proved stomach ulcers were caused by bacteria rather than stress or diet, as formerly believed. He was awarded the Nobel Prize for this discovery – confirmation that virtually the entire medical community had been wrong for decades about what caused ulcers. Such historic moments, where doctors' beliefs are summarily disproven, are infrequent. But it has happened several times during the COVID pandemic.

In media reports and the scientific literature, a recurring theme is "public misconceptions about COVID." Journalists and physicians are far less self-critical or forthcoming about their own COVID misconceptions. As the U.S. pandemic wanes we can see, with the benefit of hindsight, some things "the science" initially got wrong.

How is COVID spread? Originally, the conventional wisdom was the virus was spread primarily in two ways: first, through airborne droplets -relatively large particles- passed between people at short distances by coughing, sneezing, singing, and talking. The second route was by surface contact, i.e. touching surfaces contaminated by the virus. We now know airborne droplets are important, but surface contact is much less so. Time spent scrubbing down groceries and handling the mail with gloves was probably wasted.

Just as important as airborne droplets are aerosols – much smaller particles than droplets – primarily transmitted indoors. The critical role of aerosols was very much downplayed early in the pandemic. When there is inadequate indoor ventilation, the virus can linger in the air longer (it was probably a bad idea to discourage masked people from being outdoors in small numbers.) It illustrates the essential need for adequate ventilation in offices, schools, restaurants, gyms, etc.

How important are variants? The role of mutations in the coronavirus was initially thought to be insignificant. Mutations were believed to occur over long periods of time, and the resultant variant strains were of little clinical importance. We have learned that the virus is more prone to mutation than researchers thought. Viral variants currently represent a major source of outbreaks internationally and a recurring threat to vaccine effectiveness. Since the beginning of the pandemic, the U.S. has been behind the curve in its ability to identify variants – and continues to be so.

What role do ventilators play? In the body's struggle between virus multiplication and patients' natural virus defenses, COVID attacks the lungs and causes low blood oxygen levels. In most cases of extremely low oxygen levels, patients require a ventilator to help them breathe. That is not invariably the case; an unusual feature of COVID is that some patients can breathe adequately even in the face of low oxygen levels. By turning these patients on their stomachs (called "proning") and administering high concentrations of nasal oxygen, they can be treated successfully without resorting to ventilators. Unfortunately, early in the pandemic doctors applied ventilators indiscriminately, which damaged already compromised lungs. Thousands of patients in the U.S. and Europe probably died unnecessarily. Now we know that ventilators should be reserved for only the most advanced cases of COVID lung and that many patients will recover with temporizing measures.

What determines the mortality rate of COVID? Contrary to initial expert opinion, it is now clear that medical care is only one factor. Sophisticated medical care is important for individual patients, but industrialized countries do not necessarily have the lowest mortality. Other factors – age, previous health, genetic profile, and some unknowns are just as important, if not more so. Modern medicine should be humbled that poor countries with less access to sophisticated technology sometimes have lower COVID mortality than rich countries. (Haiti has lower mortality than Germany or the UK.)

The tragedy in medicine is not in being wrong, which is inevitable, but in refusing to acknowledge errors and failing to correct mistakes – the essence of the scientific process. In the 19th century, countless women died of puerperal sepsis because doctors ignored Ignaz Semmelweis's warning and refused to wash their hands when delivering babies.

Unanswered questions and areas of legitimate controversy abound regarding COVID including the origin of the virus; whether and how herd immunity is actually possible; the duration of immunity with infection or vaccination; and the long-term consequences of COVID. It will be many years, if ever, before studies answer those complicated questions.

In the meantime, an old adage applies to medicine, "It ain't what you don't know that gets you into trouble. It's what you know for sure that just ain't so."

Learning Empathy

Cory Franklin *Chicago Life* 7·1·21

As I write this, the United States has recorded more 550,000 COVID deaths, and the COVID vaccines, which scientists have worked on assiduously for months, are now being distributed to the general public at a rate of three million/day. One hopes that as you read this, the benefits of the vaccines will have mitigated some of the devastation of the virus.

Those are macroevents; what is sometimes lost in all this medical hurly-burly is a common microevent: the physician's duty to understand and share the feelings of the individual patient. This is commonly known as *empathy* and should be distinguished from its emotional cousin, *sympathy*. Doctors commonly feel sympathy for patients – understanding and acknowledging the discomfort and suffering the patient feels. It is hard for doctors to go through medical school without an inherent sympathy for patients.

But empathy differs from sympathy because empathy must be learned. It cannot be taught in the classroom. Understanding what a patient feels is a critical skill for physicians, and to share a patient's feelings the doctor must have had some sort of similar experience. Obviously to develop empathy for a cancer or COVID patient not every doctor must contract cancer or COVID, but the doctor will have had to have, or know someone close who has had, a severe illness. This is often not the case with young medical students and doctors who have never experienced serious illness themselves or in their families. In fact, there is literature to suggest that empathy actually declines during medical education.

Submitted for your approval, as Rod Serling used to say, a story from a long-time friend, a radiologist now approaching retirement. He told me this story recently as we commiserated about the COVID epidemic. Many years ago when he was in training, he became one of the first radiologists in the world to work with a new technology – the magnetic resonance imager, better known as the MRI. As a postgraduate physician, he worked with one of the early clinical MRI machines in the United States.

The MRI machine is essentially a huge magnet that outlines structures in the body in greater detail than its older counterparts, the X-ray or CT scanner. My friend first gained respect for the power of the machine itself when he entered the MRI suite late one evening. As he inserted his key into the door, he didn't realize the machine was on. WHOOSH! He was nearly impaled when the machine sucked his key out of the door and drove it three inches into the wall next to where he was standing. In the early days of the MRI machine patients were sometimes struck by metal objects in the suite. The protocol is now to ban all metal from the MRI area.

Fast forward 25 years. He became a respected senior radiologist in his community, one of the top doctors in his field. One morning he awoke with severe back pain. He did not know how he got it but over the course of a week, it worsened with every movement he made. Now back pain is one of the most common symptoms that doctors and surgeons evaluate, and in the course of the evaluation they commonly refer patients for an X-ray or a CT scan, and occasionally in certain situations, an MRI. Although there are many different causes of back pain, most are the result of muscular stress or minor trauma, and consequently the films do not show a cause. Most times the back pain goes away on its own with appropriate treatment. In those cases, the imaging exam, which failed to show a cause, turns out to have been unnecessary.

My friend explained to me that radiologists see many MRIs for back pain that don't reveal anything. So many that they can become slightly jaded when they encounter another MRI requisition for back pain. It's an easy trap for a radiologist to fall into the thinking that this "just another referring physician who can't be bothered to do a complete physical exam (to avoid an x-ray)" or "another 'worried well' patient exaggerating the pain, who won't take the time to ice and rest for a couple of days."

Back to my friend's back pain. It was severe and would not go away. (He acknowledged later that perhaps he did not rest like he should have.) He decided to get an MRI, concerned that it might be something more serious than muscular strain. At the same time it occurred to him that he could just be another one of those worried well patients that radiologists see so often. He got the MRI, read the films himself and was relieved that the films showed nothing out of the ordinary. Buried deep down in that relief was a bit of guilt that he had ordered an unnecessary film, an experience he was accustomed to seeing in other physicians.

But he was a professional. Despite his long history working with MRIs and 25 years' worth of experience reading MRI films, he decided to have his MRI read by one of his colleagues, who specialized in MRIs of the spine. A real professional knows when to ask for advice and yes, there are super-specialists in medicine today for almost anything.

Sure enough, his colleague spotted something he had missed – a small tear of an annulus, the outer layer of one of the spinal discs that function as rubbery cushions between the bones of the spine. It was subtle and might have gone unnoticed, but the finding in the MRI was unmistakable when it was pointed out. Annular tears occur as spinal discs dry out in the course of the natural aging process, and they can occur even with otherwise unremarkable twisting or trauma to the back. And an annular tear, even a small one, can cause excruciating back pain. With this as the explanation, my friend took it easy, with rest and medication. Eventually, the pain resolved.

Afterward, he got to thinking. What about all those patients with back pain, or some other kind of pain, who never get a diagnosis? What about those whose X-rays or lab tests are negative or the occasional situation where the doctors miss something on a film, like what almost happened to him? None of those things should diminish the fact that patients can still have real pain.

The good physician learns lessons even late in a career. Upon reflection, he concluded, "More than anything else, the whole episode taught me empathy for patients."

The tricky question of demanding kids get vaccinated to attend school

Cory Franklin Robert A. Weinstein *Chicago Tribune*
7·13·21

In Homer's "Iliad," the story of the war between the ancient Greeks and Trojans, the Greeks used a secret weapon, the Trojan horse, to vanquish their enemy at the close of a brutal 10-year conflict. In the battle against COVID-19, our own Trojan horse is vaccination. Cases and deaths have fallen dramatically since their peaks in the winter. But just as the Trojan horse did not end the threats to the Greeks, which included a pandemic during a subsequent war with Sparta, we are not out of danger either.

The United Kingdom and Israel, both with higher percentages of vaccinated populations than the U.S., have seen case surges in the unvaccinated, as well as rare breakthrough infections in those vaccinated. Israel, where cases had been as low as 25 a day, is averaging 10 times as many new cases and the country has reinstituted masking. Likewise, the U.K. is now averaging 10 times as many cases as it did during its nadir.

As long as there is a large enough pool of unvaccinated people, viral variants will emerge. The most notable is the delta variant, first discovered in India, which spread across the globe and is responsible for the current surges in Israel and the U.K. Vaccination remains in a deadly race with the emergence of these extremely contagious variants. The good news is that the variants are susceptible to the vaccine. In Israel and the U.K., vaccination has limited transmission and simultaneously suppressed most, but not all, of the deaths and hospitalizations in both countries.

In the U.S., vaccination has been amazingly effective at protecting older, high-risk individuals, but our problem lies with the unvaccinated, especially young adults who may believe the pandemic is petering out. Adults ages 18 to 29 have the lowest vaccination rate of any age group in the U.S. Fortunately, younger adults who are infected have fewer hospitalizations and lower mortality rates, although the problem of "long-haul" COVID-19 residual symptoms remains a risk. There is also the danger of spreading the virus to other unvaccinated people or to immunocompromised patients who can remain susceptible despite vaccination. If current trends continue, delta could soon become the dominant U.S. strain. Cases are already rising in parts of the U.S. where vaccination rates are low and the delta prevalence is high.

What can we do? There is no good option but to vaccinate as many as quickly as possible — ensuring vaccination of all those eligible in the U.S. and ultimately of the entire planet's population. Now we are faced with another nettlesome public health dilemma: whether to mandate vaccination of children for school attendance, as we do for other childhood vaccines.

For the safest school environment for children, vaccination must be mandatory for school staffs, who are adults in whom the vaccine has been extensively tested. But it becomes more complicated as the population cohort becomes younger. In-person learning is essential and the substantial risk of missing in-person learning must be weighed against uncertain vaccine risks. Although schools are on summer vacation, discussions should begin now on what it will take to open in the fall. And mandated vaccination for the young is on the docket.

There is no completely safe path; different countries are approaching the issue differently. In teenagers, mostly those 16-18, there has been justifiable concern about rare episodes of heart inflammation seen after receipt of the current mRNA vaccines, especially after second doses in boys. The risks after COVID-19 infection in these teenagers, including long COVID-19 and heart problems, are also rare — but more common than vaccine complications. In teenagers, the risk-benefit equation appears to come down on the side of vaccination. Data on the vaccine in children under 12, in whom the risk- benefits are still being evaluated, will become available in the next several months.

There are many unknowns about the direction of COVID-19 and the variants heading into fall. So far, the vaccines have been effective against all comers — effective enough to justify a school mandate, which would be the best way to protect our children and ensure in-person classes. But mandates sometimes flout American sensibilities and may not be universally accepted, at least not immediately. In the absence of clear-cut guidance and scientific consensus on clear-cut benefit, many schools may take the "recommend" approach for now, with the knowledge that mandated COVID-19 student vaccination may ultimately be what is required. The Centers for Disease Control and Prevention has little choice but to issue some directive before the school year starts. As it stands now, encouraging parents to do the sensible might well have greater success at getting kids vaccinated than ordering parents to do the sensible.

In the companion piece to the "Iliad," the Odyssey, the hero Odysseus must undergo a number of ordeals in order to return to his home after the Trojan War. One ordeal was to sail through a dangerously narrow straight with a terrible monster, Scylla, on one side, and a treacherous whirlpool, Charybdis, on the other. "To be caught between Scylla and Charybdis" has come to mean being trapped between two equally unpleasant alternatives.

Like Odysseus, we are facing our own Scylla and Charybdis — whether to mandate vaccination as a precondition for children to attend school.

Long COVID-19 May Have Consequences for Decades. We Need to Study It

Cory Franklin Robert A. Weinstein *Chicago Tribune* 9·17·21

William Faulkner once wrote, "The past is never dead. It's not even the past." He meant that events from the past can still affect us now or in the future. He might have been referring to COVID-19 infections, for there is growing concern that the pandemic could have its own set of health consequences years or even decades from now, so-called long COVID-19, and this may ultimately exact a huge economic and social toll on the world.

Most medical infections leave no lasting effect after patients recover, but some can cause devastating harms long after resolution. The best known is rheumatic heart disease, caused by damage to the heart valves from an inadequately treated streptococcal throat infection, otherwise known as rheumatic fever. Before the advent of penicillin, in the 1920s, rheumatic fever was the leading cause of death in the US in those 5 to 20 years old. Even for those who recovered, the infection caused heart damage in tens of thousands. Many suffered premature death from heart failure or damaged heart valves. Others, as middle-aged or elderly adults, needed heart valve replacements. (A particularly illustrative example: One of us is caring for a patient who had a heart valve replacement in 2011 for a bout of rheumatic fever in the 1930s.)

Another possible instance of long-term infectious sequela is a special form of brain inflammation, or encephalitis, that occurred during and after the influenza pandemic of 1918. (There has been debate in medical circles for years about the connection between the influenza pandemic and this type of encephalitis, but there is at least circumstantial evidence to connect the two.) It affected primarily young adults, some of whom suffered for decades with devastating neurological symptoms, including Parkinson's disease. In 1973, the eminent neurologist Oliver Sacks wrote a book about his experience with some of these encephalitis patients called "Awakenings," which was made into a 1990 Oscar-nominated movie starring Robin Williams and Robert DeNiro.

Studies have now demonstrated that a constellation of symptoms may persist for weeks, months and possibly years — we don't know yet — after recovery from COVID-19 infection. These symptoms appear to be primarily neurological (difficulty in concentration or "brain fog," headaches, depression, memory or sleep disorders); cardiovascular (heart rhythm or blood pressure problems); or related to severe fatigue. While these are the most common symptoms, virtually any organ in the body may be affected by invasion of the virus and the inflammatory response it causes. Most concerning is that no one is immune from these symptoms after COVID-19 infection — from those with the mildest cases to those who require intensive care hospitalization.

Consider that at present there have been more than 40 million cases of COVID-19 diagnosed in the US and more than 200 million worldwide. Estimates of the occurrence of long COVID-19 symptoms range from under 5% to as high as 40% of all COVID-19 cases; so, we are talking about potentially millions to tens of millions of patients, with millions more in the future. The costs — medical, rehabilitative and psychological — are incalculable. There is still ample reason to protect oneself and others through vaccination, masking and social distancing.

Without question, long COVID-19 is a real health problem, but no one is sure how much of a problem. The symptoms are nonspecific and often ill-defined. Many could be related to any acute or chronic illness — or to no illness whatsoever. That is why it is essential to perform systematic studies of long COVID-19. The scientific tools — CT scans, MRIs, computers and artificial intelligence — now exist to understand long COVID-19 and avoid the uncertainty of the question of sequelae that followed the flu pandemic when such tools were not available.

The United Kingdom has created a long COVID-19 task force. Initial data indicate that an estimated 970,000 people are experiencing long COVID-19 in the U.K. out of more than seven million diagnosed cases of COVID-19. Although several hundred thousand patients have been suffering symptoms for a year or more, only a small percentage have been referred for special care. Here in the U.S. last December, Congress provided $1.15 billion over four years for the National Institutes of Health to study the incidence, causes, risk factors and ways to prevent long COVID-19. (There is anecdotal evidence that vaccination may prevent or at least mitigate some symptoms of long COVID-19.)

The Centers for Disease Control and Prevention has also launched studies of long COVID-19, and one of the most comprehensive multistate investigations is centered here in Chicago at Rush University Medical Center. The study is attempting to enroll 4,800 patients, COVID-19-positive and COVID-19-negative, to compare the two groups. It will examine the role the virus plays in who, what, when and how often patients suffer long-haul symptoms, including a variety of the problems that can diminish the quality of life, such as fatigue and sleep disturbances. For more information on this local study, go to covidinspire.org.

We are hardly done with acute COVID-19. Many thousands of patients will die of the acute disease in the near future. It is a sobering prospect that those who survive may believe they are done with COVID-19, only to later find that COVID-19 is not done with them. Society may be dealing with this problem well into the late 21st century and in some cases perhaps even into the 22nd century.

Where COVID-19 is concerned, Faulkner's words ring true.

I once saved a man's life against his expressed wishes. Refusals to get the COVID-19 vaccine reveal the costs of stressing patient autonomy

Cory Franklin *Chicago Tribune* 9·27·21

Twenty years ago, when I was working in the intensive care unit, I saved a young man's life. He was 19 years old, and he was frothing at the mouth from life-threatening fluid filling his lungs after he injected heroin. I did nothing brilliant — I simply placed a breathing tube in his throat so he could receive oxygen through a ventilator, a routine procedure in every hospital. Two days later, he was better and walked out of the hospital. But the story wasn't so simple.

While the patient was gasping for air before I placed the tube, he told me he did not want the tube in his throat. I quickly explained to him that without the tube and the ventilator, he would die. But even as he was close to death, he was still adamant that he did not want the tube. I had to make a split-second decision, and I disregarded his wishes and placed the tube. When he left the hospital, he neither thanked me nor reproached me.

When members of my staff reviewed the case, several of them were furious with me. They vehemently disagreed with the decision to ignore his wishes and place the tube, even if it meant he died. I explained that in the heat of the moment, I felt that he was speaking out of fear and that I could not be certain that was a true expression of his wishes. Those who disagreed were unmoved — I had violated the patient's autonomy, and they were adamant that was the one sacrosanct value that doctors should never reject. Whether you agree with my decision, I bring it up to illustrate a fundamental conflict in the debate about COVID-19 vaccination, a debate that the medical community has unwittingly encouraged.

For at least 50 years, autonomy — the patient's right to determine his or her own care — has been stressed by both the medical and lay communities as the paramount value in medicine. Self-determination is embedded in the American ethos and has a long tradition in American medicine, dating to a 1914 medical negligence case. Autonomy, often restated as "my body, my decision," is the bedrock principle behind medical issues including abortion, physician-assisted death and informed consent to treatment. The field of psychiatry has undergone a revolution in the previous generation, emphasizing much greater deference to patient self-determination.

Health care ethicists and practitioners have stressed autonomy at the expense of competing values including medical paternalism, or that the doctor knows best, which is basically what I was invoking in the intubation decision; and utilitarianism or attempting to achieve the greatest good for the greatest number. For example, more people would be saved if everyone was mandated to donate one kidney to increase the number of transplantable kidneys, but kidney donation remains voluntary because we cannot and should not mandate kidney donation. Autonomy prevails.

While most patients appreciate the emphasis on self-determination, some long for the "good old days" when doctors made the decisions for patients. A number of patients have complained to me that they have asked their doctor what to do in a specific situation only to be met with the answer, "I can only give you information; I can't decide for you." The patients' frustration is understandable, but on the whole, neither medical professionals nor patients would prefer going back to the "good old days."

However, now the medical community faces a serious problem to which its members have unknowingly contributed with their long-standing wholesale emphasis on autonomy. Put simply, the consensus in this community declares that essentially all eligible Americans should be vaccinated against COVID-19. Mandated universal vaccination would certainly cut the number of COVID-19 cases and deaths dramatically. Why not take that step?

Most of the anti-vaccination arguments do not stand up to scrutiny — the vaccines have been tested and are effective, safe and can be legally mandated in many settings. But one argument many people use as part of their refusal to be vaccinated is "my body, my choice," the very principle of autonomy doctors and health care professionals have long prioritized as the cardinal virtue of medicine.

In a sense, the chickens have come home to roost. With nearly 700,000 U.S. deaths officially attributable to COVID-19, it can rightly be considered a public health emergency. In this case, autonomy might be subordinated to the greater good of the public; thousands of lives would be saved if the utilitarian argument prevailed.

But how can physicians expect everyone to turn on a dime when for decades the medical community has been hammering home the preeminence of autonomy? Only now are we realizing that the price of that message was much higher than we thought.

With COVID-19, we were too often fighting the wrong pandemic. But there are new grounds for optimism

Cory Franklin Robert A. Weinstein *Chicago Tribune*
10·11·21

If it is true that generals fight the last war and economists fight the last depression, then the COVID-19 pandemic has demonstrated that doctors fight the last pandemic. Some experts have asserted that we weren't prepared for the pandemic, but it might be more accurate to say we just weren't ready for this particular pandemic.

When COVID-19 emerged in the U.S. in late 2019 and early 2020, the public health community responded in a manner similar to how its members did in prior influenza epidemics. Two prior coronavirus outbreaks, SARS and MERS, affected virtually no one in the U.S., and influenza was the best bet for the next major pandemic. That's what the public health community geared up for.

This was an understandable approach. Alas, like Leo Tolstoy's unhappy families, each pandemic is different in its own way.

The experts were completely surprised by how COVID-19 behaved. Critically, when COVID-19 first appeared, it was often spread by patients without symptoms (asymptomatic spread) or by patients before they had symptoms (presymptomatic spread). The consequences of not appreciating viral transmission in the absence of symptoms were devastating. The virus spread rapidly in large numbers of unsuspected patients, meaning the number of cases was initially underestimated. Additionally, asymptomatic spread confounded contact tracing, normally an effective mode of controlling disease transmission.

Another surprise was that because influenza spreads through airborne droplets — from coughing, sneezing, for example — and contaminated surfaces, this was where early attention was directed for COVID-19. This diverted awareness from a key source of COVID-19 transmission: small particle aerosols that linger in poorly ventilated indoor areas. In addition, the Food and Drug Administration delayed approval of specific COVID-19 tests, essentially treating them as a doctor-to-patient diagnostic tool rather than promoting wider use for mass screening (which professional sports leagues did successfully).

But as is true of war, past reversals do not mean future defeat. We now have a new array of weapons — preventive, diagnostic and therapeutic — in our arsenal against COVID-19, and just as important, we understand our enemy better than we did in early 2020. In terms of prevention, there are now four vaccines available in the U.S., and booster shots are becoming an important adjunct. The Centers for Disease Control and Prevention director acted correctly in overruling her advisory panel and recommending broader use of boosters; in Israel, where more than three million booster doses have been administered, the protection from severe illness has resulted in Israeli cities being able to reopen.

To facilitate diagnosis, the Biden administration has announced a $1 billion investment in rapid at-home COVID-19 tests and expects that by December, 200 million rapid tests will be available each month. These tests generally identify COVID-19 positive individuals with results available in 15 minutes, and used correctly, may be useful in breaking potential infection chains in schools and businesses and at family events.

While there is still no cure for COVID-19, the most exciting development is in the realm of therapeutics. For severe COVID-19 respiratory disease, corticosteroids and other immune modulators have been demonstrated to reduce deaths. In moderate COVID-19 disease, monoclonal antibodies can forestall disease progression. Now, in a potentially revolutionary breakthrough, the drug molnupiravir has been developed for early COVID-19 disease. (An unwritten rule in the pharmaceutical industry is that new drugs must come with unpronounceable names.) Molnupiravir, now being examined by the FDA and several Asian countries, is a pill that when taken in the first five days of infection reduces the need for hospitalization. Together, these drugs represent our best hope that in the future COVID-19 will be a manageable disease at all stages.

This requires each of these weapons to be deployed efficiently. Currently, when patients receive rapid tests for influenza, positive results are poorly coordinated with effective oral treatment. To avoid repeating this snafu, the CDC should prepare protocols and indications to test patients with respiratory symptoms and when to administer treatment in patients with mild COVID-19 disease.

Of course, this means better public messaging — and a single, strong voice. To this point in the pandemic, messaging has been shambolic, too many cooks spoiling the broth. (Actually, Chicago has done a better job than federal officials, with the public health commissioner and mayor appearing together and giving coordinated public health recommendations.) The national news media are far from blameless. Too often, they have promoted sensationalism and fear over sober reporting, exacerbating public division.

As we try to recover from our initial pandemic missteps, a good model to draw on would be the Apollo space mission. In early 1967, three astronauts were killed in a launchpad fire that threatened the cancellation of the program and attempts at a moon landing. After a careful review of the tragedy, the lessons learned were instrumental in restarting the project and promoting better spacecraft design. That in turn led to the successful flight to the moon in 1969.

William Gerstenmaier, a longtime NASA engineer, who now works for Elon Musk's Space X, observed: "What we really learned from the Apollo fire, in the words of former astronaut Frank Borman, was 'the failure of imagination.' We couldn't imagine a simple test on the pad being that catastrophic. The message to the team is to remember how difficult our business is, the importance of staying focused and using our imaginations to envision what can go wrong."

Perhaps we have finally overcome our failure of imagination with COVID-19.

Is this fall downturn the end of COVID-19? Why we don't know for sure

Cory Franklin Robert A. Weinstein *Chicago Tribune*
10·25·21

The Greek historian Herodotus lived through the plague of Athens, one of the world's first great pandemics. He wrote, "Circumstances rule men; men do not rule circumstances."

So, it is with COVID-19. In the U.S., we are currently in the middle of an autumn downturn in COVID-19 cases, and no one can say whether this will be the end. It is clear, however, that the U.S. is repeating a mystifying cycle of case rise and fall that has been seen in other countries. For reasons unknown, cases surge for six to 10 weeks and then fall predictably in a similar fashion for at least an equal period.

The current wave in the U.S. began in Missouri/Arkansas in the last week of June with cases rising nationally from 13,000/day to peaking at nearly 170,000/day in early September. Case numbers have been falling since then to the current level of more than 65,000 per day. At present, we are nearing the eighth week of the downturn in cases. With luck, if the trends hold, cases are likely to fall for at least another one to three weeks. After that, no one can say what will happen. A new variant, delta-plus, has emerged sporadically, which might complicate any late-year predictions.

A similar pattern of a roughly eight-week cycle was seen this spring in India, which had the highest peak of any country in the world. The same cycle played out in Indonesia in early summer, and in Japan in the lead-up to the Olympics. Not all countries behave in this fashion; the U.K., Israel and South Korea have demonstrated somewhat different curves. But a look at worldwide case totals, the sum of the cases in every country that smooths out variations, clearly demonstrates curves consistent with the six-to-10-week cycle of rise and fall.

Why does COVID-19 behave like this? In an admission of humility somewhat surprising for COVID-19 experts, prominent U.S. public health researcher Michael Osterholm conceded, "We still are really in the cave ages in terms of understanding how viruses emerge, how they spread, how they start and stop, why they do what they do."

Because rises in cases are easier to explain, they often draw more attention than case declines. The six-to-10-week interval may be the time it takes for spread to susceptible hosts. Especially with contagious variants, dramatic surges may be fueled by 20% of infected patients — the so-called superspreaders, Nature.com suggests. Subsequent infections in the 80% of the population who are less apt to spread infection are likely to trigger greater precautions (masking, lockdowns, distancing). That, along with fewer susceptible hosts, may stop the spread — until a new cycle begins.

But peaks at six to 10 weeks followed by declines cannot be explained completely by restrictions or masking. Often, these factors are put into place even as the declines are beginning. A common error is mistaking correlation, when two events happen simultaneously, for causation, when one causes the other. Lockdowns in non-island countries have not been especially effective in halting the spread of COVID-19 except as short-term "circuit breakers."

Greater attention to case declines might yield more answers. Dramatic case declines as occurred in Japan (97% in nine weeks) and Indonesia (95% in 10 weeks) have left the experts flummoxed. Vaccination, masking and social distancing all played a factor in the downturns but are almost certainly not the primary reason.

Japan was relatively late to vaccination and never instituted a full lockdown. Kenji Shibuya, a Japanese epidemiology expert admitted as much: "Season factor, human factor and viral factor: I think that seems to be a very complicated interactional role." Earlier this year, India went from a peak of 400,000 daily cases to 40,000 daily cases in eight weeks, despite having a low vaccination rate and minimal social distancing.

Why would social behavior, so variable in different countries, result in such similar cycles of infection? We are left with two other factors, both of which we know very little about — the virus itself and host immunity. Does the virus have a built-in regulator that governs its behavior and limits it to finite cycles of infection before it retools? Can the virus, like Dracula, shut itself off at two-month intervals and reemerge in slightly different forms?

Are there different patterns of host immunity, natural and acquired, in different countries? Does immunity explain the lower rate of infection and mortality in East Asia and Africa compared to Europe and the Western Hemisphere? Is that immunity a driver in some way of the cyclical rise and fall of cases?

The medical textbooks of the next hundred years, or whatever passes for textbooks in the future, will note that the COVID-19 pandemic is the first time scientists finally have the technical resources and opportunity to investigate the crucial issue of pandemic immunity. This will be a key new area of research borne of the pandemic.

In the drama that is COVID-19, we are less the main character Hamlet than we are Rosencrantz and Guildenstern, peripheral actors at the margins of events. Unlike those courtiers, we do have some say in our collective fate. Get vaccinated, practice social distancing and mask when appropriate. In addition, ensure buildings are well-ventilated and practice good hygiene. We may not rule our circumstances, but we can help one another.

Here's the lowdown on the latest in COVID-19 medication

Cory Franklin Robert A. Weinstein *Chicago Tribune*
11·17·21

With COVID-19 cases surging in Europe and the possibility of a new late-year wave in the U.S., it is becoming clear that vaccination alone will not result in the desired effect of zero or near-zero COVID-19. In retrospect, it was probably overly optimistic a year ago to believe that at reasonably high vaccination rates, COVID-19 infections would largely be controlled.

Vaccination still remains the mainstay, but unlike the case of smallpox, it will not eliminate the virus for at least three reasons. First, there are the unvaccinated who, out of hesitation or lack of access, are present in virtually every country. Second, there are those with waning immunity post- vaccination, which is the basis for booster jabs. Finally, there are the inevitable breakthrough infections, which are currently neither predictable nor preventable. Unless some unforeseen event occurs, our goal, at least for the near future, should be to forestall the major complications of COVID-19.

With this in mind, two oral antiviral medicines that can prevent the coronavirus from reproducing in the body may soon be released for outpatient treatment of early COVID-19. This would constitute a real breakthrough. With the independent peer review and FDA approval pending, things could change, but right now here is the "what, who, where, when and why" that you should know about these drugs.

What: The first drug, Merck's molnupiravir, has already been granted conditional authorization in the United Kingdom. Merck's studies have shown the drug reduced hospitalizations and deaths by 50%. The Food and Drug Administration has been studying the drug since October and will hold hearings to review its findings on Nov. 30. The second drug, paxlovid, is from Pfizer, and the company's data indicates that it reduced the risk of hospitalization and death from severe COVID-19 in adults by 89%. These results are being independently reviewed.

Who: The drugs would be recommended as oral therapy for outpatients with COVID-19, who are either more severely ill or who have existing health conditions that put them at greater risk of hospitalization or death. There may yet be other uses for the drugs including treatment in outpatients with milder disease or as prophylactic therapy for people with known exposure to the coronavirus, but who are not yet infected. The side effects of these drugs are now being evaluated, and restrictions and precautions in certain patient groups (e.g., pregnant women) may be an important consideration when they are released.

Where: The key to these drugs is that they are outpatient therapy. Currently, the only option for outpatients with early COVID-19 at risk of serious outcome is the injection of one of the current monoclonal antibody preparations, which must be given in a health care setting, limiting their use.

The estimate right now is that the cost of a five-day course of the new medications could be in the range of $700, expensive to be sure, but less costly than administration of monoclonal antibodies and certainly less expensive than hospital care for COVID-19. It has not been determined yet whether private insurance or the government will cover the cost. Merck has already licensed molnupiravir at a cheaper price for developing countries.

When: The trials of the two new medications focused on outpatients with COVID-19 receiving treatment within five days of the onset of symptoms. This makes the availability of testing essential. Precise testing to confirm infection may take as much as 48 hours, so patients would have to receive a test within the first three to four days of symptoms. In theory, once patients suspect they have been infected, they can take a rapid 15-minute antigen test, which if positive, would lead to referral for the more precise test. If that was positive, therapy could begin.

(Symptomatic patients without access to rapid testing or those with a negative antigen test would have to visit a healthcare provider for a precise test at the onset of symptoms.) The Centers for Disease Control and Prevention and local health departments should provide practical guidelines to ensure timely testing and treatment.

Why: The first-order benefits of these new oral medications are primarily for individuals — reduced rates of hospitalization and death. But the advantages could extend beyond individual patients to preventing hospital overload, healthcare worker burnout and the adverse effects the pandemic has had on health care, inpatient and outpatient, for non-COVID-19 conditions. If, as the data suggests, these drugs minimize the ability of COVID-19 patients to infect other people, this will reduce cases in the community and bring more people back to work and school.

Prevention is always preferable to cure, and these new treatments should be viewed as an important adjunct to, not a replacement for, vaccination and essential public health control measures. Nevertheless, the option of early outpatient treatment with a course of highly effective oral medications could completely change the trajectory of the current COVID-19 resurgence, just as it did for the AIDS pandemic.

Nearly 150 years ago, Louis Pasteur, one of the legendary figures in the history of medicine and among the first to both administer vaccines and identify disease-causing microbes, said, "It is a terrifying thought that life is at the mercy of the multiplication of these minute bodies."

It is a consoling hope that science will not always remain powerless before such enemies.

A Delicate Balance

Cory Franklin *Chicago Life* 12.21.21

At the height of the last wave of the COVID epidemic, Dr. Anthony Fauci remarked that if hospitals were to get any more crowded, they would have to make tough choices about who gets an intensive care unit (ICU) bed. In the inimitable fashion of late-night television, ABC host Jimmy Kimmel, only half in jest, opined that unvaccinated patients should not be admitted to ICU. "That choice doesn't seem so tough to me. 'Vaccinated person having a heart attack? Yes, come right on in, we'll take care of you. Unvaccinated guy who gobbled horse goo? Rest in peace, wheezy.'"

Kimmel's frivolous remark aside, the idea of excluding unvaccinated patients from the intensive care unit has gained traction in serious circles. *The Washington Post* recently reported on a private memo issued by group of Texas doctors. They noted that because a patient's prognosis is part of the equation of who goes to the ICU, and vaccination reduces the chances of severe infection and death, "vaccine status therefore may be considered when making triage decisions as part of the physician's assessment of each individual's likelihood of survival." While it is true that the ICU survival of the unvaccinated is lower than that of the vaccinated, the survival of the unvaccinated is by no means prohibitively low, certainly not low enough to exclude them from the ICU, which is what the Texas doctors might have been implicitly suggesting.

I have some previous experience here. In the late 1980s, I was involved in a heated dispute with some of the country's top experts, carried out in the medical literature over whether AIDS patients should be automatically excluded from the ICU because of their (at the time) poor prognosis. Before antiretroviral drugs were developed, the survival of AIDS patients in the ICU was certainly worse than that of today's unvaccinated COVID patients.

Nevertheless survival, while low, was not prohibitive for them either. Was excluding AIDS patients from the ICU, as some hospitals were doing on the purported basis of poor prognosis, simply a convenient excuse for discrimination? Exclusion from the ICU simply could not be justified as a general policy. Eventually my side won that debate – treatments improved, patients' survival increased, and the subsequent development of antiretroviral drugs rendered the argument moot. AIDS patients were never again categorically excluded from the ICU care. (Of course, many AIDS patients, like others, elect not to have ICU care. That is their right and does not enter into this particular equation.)

112

Part of my life's work was studying ICU triage. For 30 years, I kept detailed statistics and published papers on the subject. What I discovered was that ICU triage is a devilishly complex subject - I am not sure I know that much more than when I started. One of the things I did find was that value judgments about patients should not enter into the equation. Once you start, where do you stop? The unvaccinated? Drunk drivers? Smokers? Overeaters? The elderly? *There are dragons at the end of that slippery slope.* Essentially, just as they say in the law, "you must take them as you find them."

The most cautionary tale in recent history of intermingling social values and medical treatment is the early experience with kidney dialysis in the 1960s. Seattle was the first city in the US to institute dialysis on a large scale. Because dialysis was a scarce resource at the time, the Seattle Artificial Kidney Center appointed a committee of physicians, nurses, and community and civic leaders in 1961 to determine who was eligible for dialysis treatments - and essentially who was not. The committee agreed - in all good faith - that "social worth," an assessment of the patient's anticipated contribution to society, would be the primary criterion for determining who would receive the life-sustaining treatment.

Not surprisingly, with that nebulous factor guiding the committee's decisions, candidates for dialysis turned out to overwhelmingly relatively young white males (children and those over 45 were automatically excluded at the outset). The committee was soon known as the "God panel." Journalist Shana Alexander wrote a revealing 1962 *Life Magazine* article, one of the longest the magazine ever published, that started a national controversy.

Eventually, public outrage caused this committee, and others like it formed around the country, to be disbanded. Access to dialysis was ultimately expanded, and in 1972, Congress authorized the End Stage Renal Disease Program funded by Medicare, now the nation's longest-standing entitlement program experiment and the God panel became a seminal moment in early dialysis and emerging field of bioethics.

So what should we do in times of COVID and scarce ICU beds?

The most important criteria in determining who should go to the ICU should be a combination of who is sickest, who can benefit most from the care in the ICU, and after that "first come, first served." This is not as simple as it sounds – it can be extremely difficult to determine which patient is the sickest and which one will benefit the most from ICU care (those two criteria are not always the same). This requires medical judgment, and the medical literature does not address this area in detail; there is no refence manual to refer to. Moreover, these decisions are often made in haste, late at night, and by junior physicians with the least experience. My hospital notebooks are full of the devastating consequences of wrong decisions – some made by me, many made by others.

I can't say that comparing patients for determining who should go to the ICU will never happen. It is a necessary evil that should be rare. And it should never involve making social, i.e. nonmedical, judgments about patients. There are usually other alternatives to balancing two patients, both of whom might be sick enough to require ICU care: other ICUs in the hospital, other hospitals, providing the equivalent of ICU care on the general ward, or discharging stable patients already in ICU to make more beds available.

Some would argue that the decision to get vaccinated affects not only that single person but others who might get infected – true enough. But I sincerely doubt that excluding the unvaccinated from the ICU will succeed as some sort of social experiment, becoming the dispositive factor in the decision to get vaccinated. Far more harm than benefit will accrue from such judgments in the long run. I have heard more than one healthcare professional voice the opinion that the unvaccinated don't "deserve" to get an ICU bed. It was an argument I heard many times in my ICU career about other "undesirable" patients. My response to the staff was a line from the 1992 movie, *Unforgiven*.

When the cruel sheriff, played by Gene Hackman, is about to die at the hands of a gunman, played by Clint Eastwood, Hackman tells Eastwood, "I don't deserve to die like this." Eastwood replies simply, "Deserve's got nothin' to do with it."

The U.S. has failed to follow the lead of other countries in mitigating COVID-19

Cory Franklin Robert A. Weinstein *Chicago Tribune* 1·5·22

Why aren't we paying more attention to the experience of other countries in responding to COVID-19? There is no particular country that has the answer to controlling the pandemic — unless you accept the implausible statistics from China, which claims to have only a few cases of the omicron variant in a country of 1.4 billion.

But the U.S., the world's hardest-hit country by COVID-19 in absolute terms, seems to ignore effective measures that other countries have taken to mitigate the pandemic. To our detriment, this includes efforts to make 15-minute at-home antigen tests widely available, a coherent vaccine policy and monitoring of indoor ventilation.

Many European and Asian countries have been employing rapid COVID-19 testing for over a year. These tests are not a precise diagnostic tool or a panacea, but they are quick, doable at home and reasonably accurate for identifying people who are infected, especially with repeated testing. Negative tests allow for small gatherings and safer travel. Positive tests help break potential contagion chains because a person can isolate afterward.

These tests have been shown to reduce the number of infections in other countries.

Yet it wasn't until December that President Joe Biden made it a priority for the federal government to purchase 500 million COVID-19 rapid tests for home distribution (and those tests may not be readily available for weeks). According to *Vanity Fair*, the administration rejected a plan in October to distribute free home tests. Biden has denied the report.

"It's undeniable that (the administration) took a vaccine-only approach," said rapid testing advocate Dr. Michael Mina, as reported by *Vanity Fair*. It "didn't support the notion of testing as a proper mitigation tool," said Mina, who attended the October White House meeting.

Why would the Biden administration and its public health infrastructure not embrace rapid testing? In retrospect, the testing miscalculation was part of an overly optimistic view that declining cases in early summer heralded a waning pandemic. The delay was also the result of the emphasis since early 2020 on having the medical community determine when and whom to test, as well as the desire for a level of federal regulation of testing that is greater than in other countries. However understandable, this injected a level of bureaucracy when what we need is greater efficiency.

With the emergence of omicron, the administration has backtracked, but Americans still are waiting in line or are paying exorbitant prices — if they can find home tests at all. The United Kingdom is using rapid tests to indicate whether a person is still contagious after contracting COVID-19 and to help guide isolation time. Here in the U.S., the Centers for Disease Control and Prevention has controversially shortened the isolation time for those who test positive but are asymptomatic — without recommending rapid testing for coming out of isolation.

Regarding vaccine policy, some officials at the Food and Drug Administration minimized the vaccine experience in Israel, resulting in U.S. booster recommendations being adopted belatedly. Israel has the earliest experience with vaccine distribution and documented that people receiving the vaccines demonstrated waning immunity as early as three months afterward. This was its rationale for a booster rollout for the general population (and current testing of a second booster strategy). Skepticism about Israeli data and disagreement between FDA scientists and policymakers in the Biden administration resulted in confusion and delay in administering boosters here.

Another area in which COVID-19 experience in other countries has been virtually ignored is the importance of proper ventilation for indoor activities because the airborne coronavirus is frequently transmitted in poorly ventilated rooms. The engineering community has highlighted this, and the CDC does mention ventilation as part of its COVID-19 "mitigation toolbox." But there has been virtually no emphasis or public communication on the inexpensive method to detect whether a room has adequate ventilation, which is widely used in Europe and Asia: carbon dioxide monitors. Carbon dioxide monitors, not to be confused with carbon monoxide detectors, measure and display the level of the carbon dioxide we exhale. The carbon dioxide level is an indirect indicator of how well air is circulating in a room. Room air is circulating adequately when the carbon dioxide level is low; when the carbon dioxide level is high, a window should be opened or a fan should be turned on.

The British government has subsidized carbon dioxide monitors for state-funded schools. These monitors are commonplace in commercial buildings and public venues in Europe and Japan. In places such as theaters, levels are prominently displayed on large screens informing people of the ventilation status where they are, as others enter and leave. In the U.S.? Crickets.

At this juncture, there is little to be gained by rehashing mistakes and apportioning blame. The pandemic is a global problem and far from over. Much still can be learned from other countries' experience, good and bad. The stubborn insistence of some politicians and public health experts on relying simply on what happens in the U.S. recalls the memorable line from the 2007 film "No Country for Old Men," in which the villain asks his victims before dispatching them: "If the rule you followed brought you to this, of what use was the rule?"

So many want to predict COVID-19's trajectory. But the virus has refused to cooperate

Cory Franklin Robert A. Weinstein *Chicago Tribune*
1·14·22

When it comes to the COVID-19 pandemic, it now seems that everybody is an expert, at least judging by the daily pronouncements from reporters, columnists, presidents, government officials, union officials, podcast hosts, quarterbacks, point guards, entertainers, Supreme Court justices, conspiracy theorists and anyone with a Twitter account. A bewildered public is carpet-bombed daily with statistics, predictions, mandates and advice — all delivered with supreme confidence.

In the hospital, we had a saying that an expert was "anyone from out of town who arrived with a PowerPoint presentation." Now social media, the internet and 24-hour cable mean you don't even need PowerPoint to become an "expert" and have your opinions receive widespread attention. Thus we get anti-vaxxers giving advice to drink your own urine, unvaccinated quarterbacks claiming to be immunized, Supreme Court justices giving wildly inflated infection and hospitalization numbers, and lots of people providing conflicting or confusing advice on masking, vaccines and school openings

Not to mention the terrible predictions everywhere you look. Before Thanksgiving 2020, a reporter for *The Atlantic* singled out Iowa in a scathing article about how the state could expect to see "nothing less than a tsunami" over the looming holiday season. She quoted a leading epidemiologist who assured readers, "We know the storm's coming. You can see it on the horizon." And for good measure, she interviewed four doctors and nurses who "laughed — actually laughed" at the notion that the thousands of cases might not occur. Almost on cue, the "super peak" never materialized, and cases and hospitalizations fell by 50% after the article was published. Not even an "oops!" by the reporter afterward.

Dr. Atul Gawande, the closest thing we have to a superstar doctor-author, subtly chastised Americans when he explained the relatively low COVID-19 rates in India in early 2021. "Indians have embraced masks thanks to a combination of factors, including a healthy fear of the virus among the public, a unified voice from authorities, billions of automated phone messages." Four months later, India was inundated with an average of nearly 400,000 cases a day due to the delta variant — the highest total anywhere in the world until surpassed by the current omicron surge in the U.S. Gawande never did explain how things went so wrong so quickly.

Last July, Neil Ferguson, for a time the epidemiologist who dictated Britain's COVID-19 policy, told the BBC that it was "almost inevitable" that daily infection rates would hit a record 100,000 and could peak at more than 200,000. What actually happened next was almost humorous. Cases promptly fell off to 30,000 a day. So Ferguson backtracked and predicted that the COVID-19 crisis would end by autumn. But in late autumn, his initial prediction finally came true, with the omicron variant hitting the United Kingdom, and cases did indeed peak at 200,000.

Our two pandemic-era presidents have also tried their hands at the prediction game. Donald Trump confidently predicted the pandemic would be over by Easter 2020, while Joe Biden declared victory on July 4 of last year.

Um, no.

Predictions about the course of COVID-19 are difficult, if not impossible. We've made our share of erroneous predictions about the course of the pandemic; ones we wish we could take back. Uncertainty, one of the biggest (and most constant) obstacles in medicine is downplayed too often. As onetime Secretary of Defense Donald Rumsfeld opined in another sphere, "There are known knowns. These are things we know that we know. There are known unknowns. That is to say, there are things that we know we don't know. But there are also unknown unknowns. There are things we don't know we don't know."

Observe how this affects the decisions to keep our schools open. Today, most people acknowledge the harm school closings can do to our children. We believe we can and should open schools safely. But we cannot be sure omicron and perhaps successive variants won't cause new surges in cases. We crave certainty, but our knowledge is imperfect and limited.

Another big obstacle is overconfidence. The dismal batting averages of our "expert" prognosticators should instill in them an abundance of humility. Twice, when it appeared COVID-19 was winding down, new variants — delta and omicron — appeared unexpectedly and changed the history of the pandemic. No one is expert enough to know if and when a new variant will emerge or whether new mutations will evade human defenses and result in an uncontrollable spread. Likewise, no one can be sure exactly when immunity will wane from vaccination and boosters, a development that surprised everyone in the early stages of the vaccination program. As Emory University biostatistician Natalie Dean acknowledged, "There's always this threat of curveballs."

Speaking about theoretical physics, Albert Einstein once said, "The more I learn, the more I realize I don't know." If there is anything certain about our expertise in this pandemic, it is if you think you understand COVID-19, you don't understand COVID-19.

Let's close with some optimism. Perhaps omicron is the *Gotterdammerung*, the last dramatic and apocalyptic moment on stage for COVID-19. Future variants will inevitably be controlled through vaccination, oral medications, antibody treatments and preventive measures.

No guarantees on that, though; we are not experts.

We should pivot from urging vaccination to making COVID-19 medications readily available

Cory Franklin Robert A. Weinstein *Chicago Tribune*
1·24·22

Two years ago, "pandemic" became a household word. Today, the lethal contagion refuses to concede. The omicron wave in the U.S. peaked in mid-January and is beginning to decline, but the country still averages more than half a million new cases and more than 1,500 deaths every day, both of which are easily the highest totals in the world.

We have focused intently on prevention, less so on treatment. Now it is imperative to devote greater national attention to reducing COVID-19 morbidity and mortality, beyond simply encouraging vaccination. Americans would benefit if politicians and healthcare professionals energetically promoted the new effective COVID-19 medications. Without this overdue pivot, thousands of lives may be lost unnecessarily this spring.

In COVID-19 treatment, as in life, timing is everything. One painful lesson we learned early in the pandemic is that the longer we wait to treat infected patients, the less successful those treatments are — early is good, earlier is better. There are now medications for those not yet infected and for those with symptomatic COVID-19. These medications are not a substitute for vaccination in vaccine-eligible patients, but we must facilitate the use of these drugs as an added level of protection.

Not everyone is familiar with the new prevention and treatment options, which represent a remarkable scientific development. Let's walk through them. For patients not yet infected but who have weakened immune systems or who cannot be vaccinated for any reason — such as an allergy or previous reaction — the medication Evusheld provides protection against COVID-19 infection. If infected, patients with weakened immune systems have higher rates of hospitalization and death, so Evusheld can be the preferred treatment after exposure to COVID-19.

Bureaucratic problems remain. Evusheld is a monoclonal antibody, a drug that must be administered through injection or intravenously. This entails a clinic visit by the patient or a home health visit by a nurse. Experience with previous monoclonal antibodies saw some hospitals and doctors view this treatment as a relative inconvenience, tying up beds or staff. This led to woeful underuse of the medications, which were often discarded without being used.

In addition, supplies of Evusheld are currently being rationed; only people with the weakest immune systems are eligible recipients. The federal government replenishes states' supplies of the drug based, in part, on use. The less you use, the less you may receive. Essentially, rationing the drug may create shortages. Restricting the use of the drug, rather than using it for those in immediate need, will mean unused medications sitting on the shelf, destined to become outdated and useless. Expanding use will improve coordination from testing through receiving medication, so priority tiers and restrictions around Evusheld should be removed.

For anyone who has recently become infected and not sick enough to be hospitalized, the new oral medication Paxlovid is effective in preventing COVID-19 complications. The logistical problem is that Paxlovid must be taken within five days of onset of COVID-19 symptoms. How is a medical professional or office to get a symptomatic patient tested, diagnosed and then able to receive a prescription and medicine in that time?

This entails medical care provider and patient education. Illinois provides online access to reputable testing sites, and home test kits should include an instruction card on what to do and whom to notify for those testing positive. Lab-based test results should be available to patients and providers within one day and include similar instructions.

Quick sharing of results would let doctors order prescriptions right away and would help pharmacists control their inventory so drugs are always available. Doctors and pharmacists can check online for possible dangerous interactions between the new drug and each patient's existing prescriptions. Again, the goal is to develop fast, efficient pathways from testing to receiving medication. Here in Chicago and Illinois, officials have begun facilitating this pipeline.

For those who have contracted COVID-19, a new monoclonal antibody, Sotrovimab, is especially effective against the omicron variant. Sotrovimab must be given within 10 days of symptoms. Because of still-limited availability, there is a similar tier system to that of Evusheld. Federal agencies, providers and pharmacies should streamline the process.

One more imperative: To this point, hospitals and doctors have concentrated on inpatient rather than outpatient COVID-19 care. Expanding outpatient care demands more of providers but could curtail the pandemic. With the new treatments available, public health departments should consider consolidating the testing-to-medication progression in temporary regional outpatient centers. Such a center would test a person, and, if the results are positive, call the person's doctor's office and request a prescription, assuming the patient's health history permits. If it does, the patient picks up the pills right after his or her results come back.

So far, vaccinations have been effective, but vulnerable to an implacable, wily enemy. The new COVID-19 medications are our defense in depth. Our politicians and public health professionals should deploy them urgently.

Remember: We're averaging more than 500,000 new cases, and 1,500 deaths, every day.

COVID-19 isn't the only reason more people are dying at this time

Cory Franklin Robert A. Weinstein *Chicago Tribune*
2·15·22

In addition to sickness, suffering and death, pandemics wreak havoc in the societies they afflict. Smallpox helped destroy the Aztec Empire, and the Black Death completely changed the social fabric of Europe in the Middle Ages. Sometime early this spring, the U.S. death total for the COVID-19 pandemic will pass the one million milestone, but this grim number is not an accurate tally of the devastation wrought by the virus. Any comprehensive account must include other deaths, specifically those that have occurred as a result of the social disruption caused by our reaction to COVID-19.

In a recent online news conference, Scott Davison, CEO of the insurance company OneAmerica, said that in the first three quarters of 2021, the death rate among working-age people was 40% greater than pre-pandemic levels. "We are seeing, right now, the highest death rates we have seen in the history of this business — not just at OneAmerica. The data is consistent across every player in that business." Davison said the 40% increase in deaths was primarily in those ages 18 to 64. "Just to give you an idea of how bad that is, a three-sigma or a one-in-200-

year catastrophe would be a 10% increase over pre-pandemic," he said. "So 40% is just unheard of."

The excess deaths result from a wide array of causes. Some are people who died from diagnosed COVID-19, some are people who died of undiagnosed COVID-19 and some deaths are attributed to COVID-19 when it was not the primary cause (e.g., a suicide in which someone is COVID-19-positive). But the deaths most difficult to tally, and arguably the most troubling, are non-COVID-19 deaths that provide a window into problematic social issues related to the pandemic.

Overdose deaths, especially related to fentanyl and its derivatives, are now at record levels in the US. In the first half of 2021, there were also more motor vehicle fatalities recorded than in any previous six-month period. Homicides, especially in urban areas, have risen as well. Add to this the deaths of people who have not had access to care for serious chronic conditions such as heart disease and cancer, and those people who have been reluctant to visit hospitals and clinics out of fear of COVID-19 infection. There is ample evidence that the number of excess deaths during the pandemic — that is, deaths beyond the number that typically occur in a specific time frame — has disproportionately come from Black, Latino and Native American communities.

Regarding lockdowns, a controversial new working paper, sourced out of Johns Hopkins University by three economists, has suggested lockdowns did relatively little to minimize deaths from COVID-19. The study has yet to be peer-reviewed, and critics will undoubtedly be debating the conclusions for years, long after the pandemic is over. But at this point, no one can deny the profound social, economic and personal impact lockdowns have had.

Based on the historical experience with pandemics, this level of social dislocation has disturbingly comparable precedents. Perhaps the earliest recorded was 2,600 years ago during the Peloponnesian War between the city-states of Sparta and Athens. At the height of the conflict, an unknown plague befell Athens, killing nearly a third of the population. The great Athenian historian Thucydides, who chronicled the war and the plague, gave a stirring description of human nature during the epidemic, which has striking parallels with today's world.

"The plague marked the beginning of a decline to greater lawlessness in the city. People were more willing to dare to do things which they would not previously have admitted to enjoying when they saw the sudden changes of fortune ... so they thought it reasonable to concentrate on immediate profit and pleasure. ... No one was willing to persevere in struggling for what was considered an honorable result. ... What was pleasant in the short term, and what was in any way conducive to that, came to be accepted as honorable and useful. No fear of the gods or law of men had any restraining power. ... No one expected to live long enough to have to pay the penalty for his misdeeds: people tended much more to think that a sentence already decided was hanging over them, and that before it was executed, they might reasonably get some enjoyment out of life."

Consider that account, from the fifth century B.C., and imagine all those Americans who have died from fentanyl overdoses. Or think about the motorist careening past you at 95 mph on the highway, primed for a fatal rollover. Self-destructive choices and social upheaval have killed untold thousands of risk-takers. And that's in addition to the nearly one million Americans who have succumbed to the virus.

The pandemic highlights a global failure to protect the elderly

Cory Franklin Robert A. Weinstein *Chicago Tribune*
3·14·22

When the COVID-19 pandemic finally ends, our most glaring failure, and our greatest source of shame, will unquestionably be our unwillingness to protect society's most vulnerable group: the elderly. The 65 years and older cohort makes up only a little more than 15% of the U.S. population but accounts for more than 75% of all COVID-19 deaths, a significant increase in elderly deaths over recent non-pandemic years.

This breakdown in care has been especially glaring in our nursing homes, which are often referred to as residential care facilities. The Centers for Disease Control and Prevention reported that there have been over one million COVID-19 cases in American nursing homes (1.2% of total U.S. cases) and more than 151,000 deaths (16% of total U.S. COVID-19 deaths, which does not include the far larger number of deaths in the elderly who died outside of nursing homes). The 15% COVID-19 mortality rate in nursing home residents is 12 times the national average. Caregivers in these facilities have also suffered disproportionately, with another one million cases in nursing home workers and over 2,300 deaths.

When government and public health officials ultimately sit down to review their responses to the pandemic, one of the first things they should revisit is the lack of strict institutional control measures at the local, state and federal levels. This, combined with the appalling decision by some governors to return infected patients to nursing homes who might still be contagious, was the predicate for high death counts, especially early in the pandemic.

Even today, we continue to disregard best practices: More than 10% of nursing home patients remain unvaccinated, and greater than 25% have not received a booster. (Also, more than half of nursing home staff members nationwide have not received boosters.) This travesty is by no means exclusively an American fiasco; it is occurring in most industrialized countries worldwide. Now another country, one that was once acclaimed for its COVID-19 control policies, is reaping a similar catastrophic whirlwind.

Hong Kong, which had been pursuing a zero-COVID-19 strategy from the beginning of the pandemic, has been rocked by a recent surge from the omicron variant that is as devastating as anywhere in the world. For the first two years of the pandemic, Hong Kong had a total of roughly 13,000 cases. Since Jan. 1, cases have gone up nearly 40-fold and have now passed 600,000. This omicron surge is not the benign wave that is commonly described — in the last month, Hong Kong has had the highest per capita death rate in the world. On Jan. 1, there were 200 total deaths over the first two years of the pandemic. In the last month, there have been 3,000.

Just as in the U.S., omicron has torn through the majority of Hong Kong nursing homes, infecting residents and staffers at a dramatic rate. And although Hong Kong has one of the top vaccination rates of any country in the world, only 15% of its nursing home residents have been vaccinated. Nine out of 10 COVID-19 deaths in Hong Kong have occurred in the unvaccinated, the majority of whom are 70 years old or older.

Yuen Kwok-yung, a University of Hong Kong microbiology professor and government adviser on COVID-19, was spot-on in a recent interview: "It would have been better if (the elderly) were vaccinated in the past eight months. We could have avoided this huge problem now. ... Unfortunately, I think the elderly will pay a huge price."

This is at once a public health failure and a societal failure. Every pandemic singles out members of vulnerable groups who require greater protection, generally those at the extremes of age. COVID-19 is unusual in that children have been relatively spared; it is the elderly who need more resources and attention. Amid the hurly-burly of lockdowns, anti-vaxxer pushback, social distancing and mask mandates, this basic public health principle has been relatively ignored. But the pandemic has also pulled back the veil on our reprehensible treatment of the aged. The practice of shuttling the elderly out of sight and out of mind has replaced the biblical commandment of honoring father and mother.

The omicron wave is receding in the U.S., even as an average of 1,000 people still die daily and the one-millionth U.S. death will be recorded in the next month. The good news is that this death rate will almost certainly decline in the next month, reflecting the recent lower case totals, but the bad news is we cannot rule out another wave of infections in the spring. Already, Western Europe is seeing new case rises that may reflect waning vaccine immunity, the new BA.2 variant or a combination of the two.

This new wave may not come to the U.S., but if it does, we must prioritize protecting our elderly much more than we do now. This will entail increasing vaccination rates and COVID-19 testing in nursing homes, as well as facilitating access to anti-COVID-19 oral medications for the elderly. But it demands something else as well — encouraging a newfound respect for the elderly. It is the mark of a humane and responsible society.

There is much we still don't know about giving 5 to 11-year-olds a COVID-19 vaccine

Cory Franklin Robert A. Weinstein *Chicago Tribune*
3·28·22

Should children ages 5 to 11 receive the COVID-19 vaccine? This is a difficult question without an easy answer, something you wouldn't know from the strident opinions of politicians and health experts.

On one side are the Centers for Disease Control and Prevention, the American Academy of Pediatrics and Pfizer, which makes the only approved vaccine for children. They have all recommended vaccination for children ages 5 and older. On the other side is the state of Florida. Florida's Department of Health, at odds with most public health officials, does not recommend the shots for children. That agency said focus should be on youngsters with existing health conditions as "the best candidates for the COVID-19 vaccine" and that some healthy children "may not benefit from receiving the currently available COVID-19 vaccine."

Florida Surgeon General Joseph Ladapo said the decision should be made on an individual basis, rather than mandated. Ladapo did not specify what qualifies a child as "healthy" nor did he note the specific age group to which agency guidelines pertain.

In Washington by contrast, White House press secretary Jen Psaki, who recently contracted COVID-19 despite being vaccinated, articulated the Biden administration's position: "We know the science. We know the data and what works and what the most effective steps are in protecting people of a range of ages from hospitalization and even death."

This is a nuanced issue, and context matters. Children are certainly at risk from COVID-19 — at the beginning of the pandemic in 2020, children accounted for fewer than 3% of cases; today, they account for about 25%. More than six million U.S. children have contracted COVID-19, including two million ages 5 to 11. Any COVID-19 infection, no matter how trivial, creates the possibility of disruption of home and school activity.

But there are several important distinctions because children and adults show fundamentally different immune responses to COVID-19 in their airways and blood. Even with a surge caused by the omicron variant (currently declining in the U.S.), severe illness among infected children is rare: the death rate for Americans under age 18 is roughly 1 in 10,000 infections, primarily in those with comorbidities including obesity, diabetes, cancer and other chronic conditions.

For healthy children, the balance is different. The CDC has documented tens of thousands of hospitalizations in children with COVID-19. Although about one-third did not have existing health conditions, hospitalizations were less frequent in children 5 to 11 than in those under 5 or in teenagers. Each age group shows different outcomes. (If the new Moderna vaccine is approved, the vaccination question will extend to children 6 months to 5 years old.)

The data from the United Kingdom for children 5 to 11 is infrequently cited in the U.S. but is telling: Vaccination would be estimated to prevent 113 admissions to intensive care units per million vaccinated high-risk children in a future severe COVID-19 wave, but only three ICU admissions per million in low-risk children. In a less severe COVID-19 wave, the number of prevented ICU admissions for healthy children might be as low as 0.5 per million. Extrapolating from the math, 5 to 11-year-olds are not the same as those younger or older. In addition, the distinction between healthy children and those with chronic conditions is significant.

High-risk children ages 5 to 11 should unquestionably be vaccinated for the same reason adults should be vaccinated — to minimize the serious outcomes of COVID-19 infection. In healthy 5 to 11-year-olds, the incidence of complications is extremely low, so the issue is whether the vaccine prevents children from acquiring and transmitting the virus. The most recent Pfizer data for children 5 to 11 in New York shows that the effectiveness of vaccination in preventing infection decreased during the omicron surge, to a mere 12% from a previous 68%. That finding raises new questions about whether to vaccinate healthy kids in this age group.

None of this means that 5 to 11-year-olds should not be vaccinated; merely, that scientists aren't sure about the level of protection provided by the vaccine. Maybe the dose of Pfizer vaccine tested for children was too low. There is also uncertainty as to whether the vaccine dose for 5 to 11-year-olds should be based on age, weight or an evaluation of the maturity of the child's immunity.

Initial data indicates the vaccine is safe in children — the complication rate is extremely low. But because the complication rate of COVID-19 in healthy 5 to 11-year-olds is also low, it is difficult to compare both and draw a definitive conclusion, especially with different school mask mandates across the country confounding the question. A minority of children 5 to 11 in Europe have currently been vaccinated.

The typical risk-benefit of vaccination for COVID-19 is different for the diseases we were immunized for as children. There has been little genetic evolution and few variants for diseases like chickenpox. The vaccines for those diseases have proved safe and effective for decades.

We have not reached that point with the COVID-19 vaccine for 5 to 11-year-olds. We need more data collection, more scientific debate and less inflamed political rhetoric.

For now, the decision remains with the parents. One of us has recommended that his grandchildren be vaccinated. The other is waiting for more information.

Have we become too reliant on deferring to experts?

Cory Franklin *Chicago Tribune* 4·11·22

In one of the most dramatic moments of the Senate confirmation hearing for Supreme Court nominee Ketanji Brown Jackson, Sen. Marsha Blackburn asked the judge, "Can you provide a definition for the word 'woman'?" After a brief hesitation, Jackson responded, "I'm not a biologist." Now on its face, that is a silly remark because you don't need a biologist to define what a woman is. (The percentage of babies born with indeterminate sex, in which a medical evaluation is necessary, is less than 1%). But upon consideration, it was actually a clever response because it was basically the only answer available to Jackson that would avoid enraging either the Republican senators or her progressive allies. It was a prudent nonanswer.

Yet, putting aside for a minute her predicament before the Senate, Jackson's answer provides a window into the current role conferred on experts and how reliance on experts may be encroaching into territory that was once within the purview of common sense. For those on Twitter who are waiting to pounce with a charge that I'm minimizing the importance of experts, let me state the obvious: A functioning society depends on experts. They are indispensable to every profession for tasks ranging from developing essential software to building bridges to performing cardiac surgery. But in an ever more complex society, have we run the risk of becoming overly dependent on experts — delegating decisions and responsibilities to them that are outside their domain?

The danger is quite simply this: Experts are human. Some are modest and self-effacing; others crave attention, money and power. When the latter group enters the public forum because "we rely on them," there is trouble ahead. Politicians court their favor and flatter them with public moneys and posts that are often little more than sinecures. In return, those politicians use their expert opinions to advance political aims.

There is an aphorism that if you put a cup of soup in a bowl of garbage, it's garbage. And if you put a cup of garbage in a bowl of soup, it's garbage. Along those lines, if you inject politics into science, it's politics. And if you inject science into politics, it's politics. When politics become a consideration, the temptation for experts to abandon objective interpretations of scientific data is undeniable. Witness how during the first months of the COVID-19 pandemic, public health authorities deemed some political rallies safer than others based on nothing other than the cause the rally supported. No matter that in any case, tens of thousands of people who practiced limited distancing came from all over the country to shout and chant, thereby possibly spreading the virus. Experts determined that in terms of safety, what mattered was the cause. There was nothing scientific about that.

The situation becomes even more parlous when experts are permitted to make public policy, and governments hide behind those they appointed. Margaret Thatcher once said, "Advisers advise, ministers decide." But during the COVID-19 pandemic, not only the United Kingdom but also the U.S. and most of the world seemed to eschew that dictum. In retrospect, the plan of public health authorities to lock down society "to flatten the curve" seems to have been a monumental act of hubris, considering the effects on the economy and especially on young people. The public health community failed to recognize that others like economists and business leaders had to be consulted to assess the complex trade-offs.

The best illustration of what can happen when expertise morphs into a political tool is when Soviet leader Josef Stalin made one scientist, Trofim Lysenko, the arbiter of all Soviet agricultural science in the 1930s. Any scientist who criticized him was criticizing the Communist Party and the state itself. That political faith in Lysenko's junk science caused mass starvation and the destruction of the careers of many dissenting but honest Soviet scientists. It slowed the progress of Soviet science for decades.

We have crossed the Rubicon regarding our dependence on experts when a smart, Harvard-educated Supreme Court justice cites the need for a biologist to define womanhood. Think how far afield this is from 1965, when Bob Dylan penned a seminal lyric for the Vietnam generation: "You don't need a weatherman to know which way the wind blows."

Dylan was in effect telling a rebellious Vietnam generation not to place too much faith in experts — use your common sense in your efforts to bring down the establishment. Today, society has done a 180 — the Vietnam generation is now the establishment, and employing experts is a key tactic to asserting authority and, in some case, to infantilizing the public.

To be "guided by the science" should never be an excuse for us to blindfold ourselves willingly in deference to expert opinion.

China's surge proves the folly of trying to achieve 'zero-COVID-19'

Cory Franklin Robert A. Weinstein *Chicago Tribune*
4·14·22

From the outset, mystery has shrouded the COVID-19 pandemic in China. The origin of the virus remains unknown, important Chinese journalists and key scientists have been muted, and case and death totals reported by China's government have been unbelievably low — the United States and most of Western Europe have reported 500 to 1,000 times as many per capita deaths as China.

There are several theories on the reason for the low numbers coming out of China: poor reporting, deliberate or otherwise; a population with immunity, either natural or acquired through previous coronavirus infections; or the Chinese government's efforts to reach zero COVID-19 infections through mass testing, lockdowns, quarantine and contact tracing. China is the last major country attempting to eliminate COVID-19; other countries have tried with disappointing, and in some cases disastrous, results.

But now the Chinese zero-COVID-19 policy has been put to the test by the highly infectious omicron variant and subvariant. The focal point is the tight government lockdown in China's largest city, Shanghai. Reports emanating from Shanghai are harrowing. People are prevented from leaving their homes for any reason — they are dependent on the government to deliver medications, food and water. Parents who test positive are sent to isolation centers, separated from their children. Cats and dogs left homeless when their owners are sent away are being killed by public health authorities. Businesses are closing, and there are reports of people scavenging food and committing suicide.

According to the BBC, centralized "isolation facilities — many using only camp beds, with no showers or other facilities — are bursting with infected people squashed in next to one another. One of China's few reliable media outlets, Caixin, has reported that close contacts of infected people will be moved to neighboring provinces. This could potentially involve hundreds of thousands of Shanghai residents." Even with these measures, Shanghai is reporting more than 10,000 new cases per day, and things may worsen because China's vaccine, a non-mRNA one, appears to be less effective than Western vaccines.

While China clings to its zero-COVID-19 approach, other countries have abandoned it in the face of the omicron surge. South Korea, which was praised internationally for its control measures after an initial surge, was overwhelmed by omicron and now ranks eighth in worldwide cases, a higher per capita case rate than the U.S. New Zealand, an island country, that as of February had recorded fewer than 30,000 cases over the first two years of the pandemic, now has seen 800,000 cases total. Hong Kong, with only 200 total deaths during the pandemic at the beginning of the year, had the highest per capita death rate in the world in March.

Why has a zero-COVID-19 policy proved unattainable? Control of COVID-19 poses different problems from previous epidemics. The virus is evolving and mutating at a surprisingly rapid rate, and the current variants present a greater risk of person-to-person transmission. But the real sticking point has been extensive transmission in the community by infected people who are asymptomatic. This feature of COVID-19 has complicated the pandemic from the beginning. It makes it problematic to know whom to test and whom to isolate.

Contact tracing, a basic public health tool used successfully for previous communicable diseases — especially those sexually transmitted — is basically impossible. Contact tracing works when symptomatic patients seek care, enter the public health surveillance tracking system and identify their contacts. Those exposed to contagious individuals are then located and advised about quarantine, testing and treatment options. But millions of dollars and a lot of personnel have been ineffective in tracing COVID-19 when asymptomatic patients are unaware they should be tested or fail to report a positive if they test at home. The contacts of those infected are often unknown, especially when the virus is spread in crowded indoor locations.

South Korea employed the most extensive contact tracing system in the world but abandoned it recently in the face of the omicron surge. Jang Young-ook, a researcher at the Korea Institute for International Economic Policy studying pandemic response policies around the world, said, "The size of the surge Korea is seeing now renders contact tracing almost pointless. That makes collecting personal information with QR (computerized personal) codes kind of unjustified." This is basically an admission that zero COVID-19 is a pipe dream, a lesson the residents of Shanghai are learning the hard way.

When the definitive history is written about the COVID-19 pandemic of the early 2020s, an essential chapter will be the futile quest for zero COVID-19. It will be symbolized by a drone hovering over deserted Shanghai streets, blaring the disheartening epitaph for zero COVID-19 that China has been broadcasting to its people: "Please comply with COVID restrictions. Control your soul's desire for freedom. Do not open the window or sing."

The next phase of addressing COVID-19 in children? Accepting it as part of life

Mary Hall Cory Franklin *Chicago Tribune* 4·27·22

Whether it is attending school, being vaccinated or transmitting the virus at family gatherings, the role of children in the COVID-19 pandemic has been contentious and widely debated, not just in the United States but across the world. Two years in, what have we learned and what can we apply to the future concerning children and COVID-19?

When the threat of COVID-19 emerged in early 2020, pediatricians braced to provide care for a flood of sick children across the country. A pediatric clinic is normally a busy place, especially during the protracted viral respiratory season, October to May, when it is typical for small children to annually experience as many as 10 colds caused by endemic respiratory viruses.

Fortunately, in most situations, healthy children recover from respiratory viruses within a week with supportive care and endemic human respiratory viruses becoming permanent members of our viral ecosystem. But COVID-19 was an unknown wild card. It turned out to be a pleasant surprise when it became clear the coronavirus caused milder illness in children than adults. For healthy young patients, with rare exceptions, this has essentially remained true throughout the pandemic.

But there was another intriguing and unexpected surprise as well.

In the first year of the pandemic, COVID-19 turned out to be milder in children, but colds, ear infections, wheezing episodes and stomach bugs also seemed to disappear. The frequency of common viral illnesses expected in the youngest patients plummeted. Initially, it was believed that parents were simply reluctant to bring children in, but greater numbers of parents reported, with considerable relief, that their children were just not getting sick.

This temporary disappearance of most endemic pediatric viruses was partly the result of behavior changes, particularly the cancellation of in-person meetings, group activities and travel plans. However, pandemic mitigations could not be the entire explanation because the same disappearance was observed in areas where children attended school or uninterrupted day care.

Eventually, with the onset of the highly contagious omicron wave last winter, more and more children were infected with COVID-19, most with mild symptoms. The Centers for Disease Control and Prevention estimates that as of February 2022, approximately 75% of children and adolescents have been infected, with approximately one-third of those infections coming since December 2021. Including those who have been vaccinated, there is now considerable population immunity to the virus in children.

In the past year, a rebound in routine childhood viruses has occurred during the intervals when COVID-19 waves ebbed. The typical viral respiratory illnesses are spreading again, with the expected natural cycle of waning in May and returning in autumn. Parents and teachers once again confront maintaining public health measures meant to avoid the spread of viral illnesses with the priority of the educational, developmental and emotional needs of children. The key is to offer kids routine protection against common diseases (staying home when sick, washing hands) — not frantic overprotection against one illness in particular.

The pediatric immune system is programmed to encounter a new virus and generate an initial immune response. Anyone who has spent time with toddlers is familiar with their desire to touch and lick everything. This type of exploration plays many roles in child development, and one may include immunologic development.

Small children sample the viral environment, which in turn enables them to mount an immune response. Children eventually augment the response with subsequent exposures, eventually resulting in a mature, adult immune system. It is beneficial for children to be exposed to routine viral illnesses that inevitably spread and ultimately recede. Acceptance of this reality will be important in preventing unnecessary disruptions to children's lives.

Viruses interact with each other and with our immune systems. Some of these interactions may be advantageous for unknown reasons. On occasion, wide spread of one virus can crowd out other viruses, a phenomenon known as viral interference. This happened in 2009 when an incipient influenza pandemic was short-circuited by an endemic rhinovirus outbreak. Was this what happened in the first year of the COVID-19 pandemic? If so, the return of endemic viruses and unpleasant, but benign, colds may be an encouraging sign that the COVID-19 pandemic is finally subsiding.

In the New Testament, Jesus says, "Let the little children come to me, and do not hinder them, for the kingdom of God belongs to such as these." As parents, pediatricians and other professionals who love children, we should guard against becoming overprotective. For children to develop the robust immune systems required for healthy adulthood, we must recognize that viral illnesses are a necessary part of life.

The US response to COVID-19 hasn't been a train wreck. We're just average

Cory Franklin Robert A. Weinstein *Chicago Tribune* 5·2·22

The COVID-19 pandemic has taken another turn with new variants BA.2 and BA.2.12.1, which are apparently more contagious but less severe than their predecessors, causing a new mini-wave of infections in the U.S. Nationally, cases are up, but deaths and hospitalizations remain relatively low for now. Amid what amounts to an emerging sixth wave, the U.S. has received disproportionate criticism at home and from international observers for its handling of the pandemic. But over recent months, events worldwide should dispel notions of exceptional American malfeasance.

You probably haven't seen some of these things reported about the pandemic:

At more than 82 million, the U.S. still has by far the most diagnosed cases of any country. But in the last year, a number of advanced nations have had much greater case rises than the U.S. and now have higher case levels adjusted for population size. Since the beginning of May 2021, diagnosed COVID-19 cases in the U.S. have gone from roughly 33 million to 82 million — a rise of about 150%. In the same interval, cases in the United Kingdom have gone up by 300%; in France, 400%; in Germany,

600%; in Japan, 1,400%; and in South Korea, the rise has been an astronomical 13,500%.

All these countries except for Japan now have a higher per-capita case rate than the U.S., which is an adjustment for population size. Even Sweden, which is often cited as a model for containment of the pandemic, has had a greater case rise than the U.S. in the last year and now has a similar per-capita case rate.

With total COVID-19 deaths here approaching one million, the U.S. also has more deaths than any other country in the world. But when adjusted for population size, the U.S. ranks 16th in the world in deaths per capita. Most of the countries with more per-capita deaths are in Eastern Europe — Hungary, Croatia and Lithuania — along with two South American countries, Peru and Brazil. If crude mortality is considered independent of the population — that is, deaths per number of diagnosed cases since the start of the pandemic — at 1.2%, the U.S. is squarely at the world average, neither especially high nor low. The figures do not suggest the U.S. stands out from the crowd.

In the face of new variants, COVID-19 cases and especially COVID-19 deaths are dropping dramatically worldwide. Right now, there are fewer than 2,500 deaths per day worldwide — down more than 85% from the peak and the lowest level since the early days of the pandemic in

March 2020. This drop in worldwide deaths is a reason for long-term optimism. The current U.S. decline in deaths has been substantial: This country is incurring a lower percentage of worldwide deaths than at any time previously in the pandemic.

However, the U.S. is still responsible for a higher percentage of the world's deaths than any other country (16%). This is obviously not because of poorer medical care and is unlikely to be because of worse management of the pandemic. It is probably the result of less prior immunity in the U.S. than elsewhere, as well as a higher percentage of high-risk patients, i.e., elderly, immunocompromised or obese.

U.S. vaccination rates are within a few percentage points of those in most Western European countries, and a link between vaccination and death totals does not explain why U.S. deaths were also comparatively higher throughout most of 2020, before vaccines were available. Despite low vaccination rates, every African country has a lower per-capita death rate than those in the U.S. and most wealthy Western European countries.

Vaccination unquestionably reduces any single COVID-19 patient's chances of death but does not translate easily to a nation's reduced death rates. Two of the countries with the world's highest vaccination rates, Brazil and Peru, also have among the highest per-capita death rates. Rate of vaccination is only one aspect of immunity. Native immunity and previous COVID-19 infection are also important determinants of response to COVID-19. Even within vaccination rates, a whole host of variables are important: type of vaccine, number of doses, the interval between doses and time since last dose.

None of this is to take the U.S. off the hook in its handling of the pandemic. Both the Trump and Biden administrations declared victory way too early. For too long, the public health community put most of its faith in vaccine research; therapeutics were almost an afterthought. This wasn't necessarily a bad strategy, but the rapid and unexpected emergence of variants rendered it less effective than anticipated. The Centers for Disease Control and Prevention and many public health agencies nationwide have been clumsy in marshaling their response to this viral evolution. Partisan politics often influenced what should have been the straightforward science of epidemiology: what, exactly, is happening and what should we do about it. As a result, there have been too many contradictory or inaccurate statements by too many government officials.

Despite what you may read or hear, the U.S. has done no better or worse than most other countries. We Americans have no cause to wave the flag nor to hang our heads.

The current state of COVID-19 should invite hope — not complacency

Cory Franklin Robert A. Weinstein *Chicago Tribune* 6·3·22

The famous Robert Frost poem "The Road Not Taken" begins: "Two roads diverged in a yellow wood, / And sorry I could not travel both." The United States and the rest of the world faced a fork in the road with two possible options at the outset of the COVID-19 pandemic: Attempt to control the spread of the virus through social measures and lockdowns or let the virus run its course naturally ("let it rip," as some have referred to it) in the hope of inducing herd immunity in the populace.

Countries selected one path or the other, and neither strategy was completely successful. The "flatten the curve" approach in the U.S. failed to prevent virus spread and resulted in large numbers of COVID-19 and non-COVID-19 deaths while simultaneously damaging the economy and harming childhood education. The "let it rip" approach, employed by Sweden, produced marginally better results — roughly the same number of cases per capita as the U.S., less economic downturn and fewer excess deaths — but was hardly an unqualified success. (Deaths per capita are higher in Sweden than in the other Scandinavian countries.)

So, facing our next crossroad, as the sixth wave in the U.S. may be starting to wind down, how best to return to a "normal life"?

The COVID-19 virus has shown it is nimble in mutating, spreading and circumventing vaccine and acquired immunity. This makes the cost of attempting to suppress infections by once again closing schools and instituting lockdowns unacceptably high. Children have already suffered immeasurably, and lockdowns would further cripple the business sector. Nor would this likely work; even the draconian zero-COVID-19 measures of Communist China and North Korea have proved futile in the face of the current, extremely contagious variants.

Alternately, as new variants become more communicable but less severe (current COVID-19 mortality is 90% lower than it was in early 2020), we can hope this unprecedented rapid viral evolution results in a version of COVID-19 that resembles the common cold. Adapting to it would mean living with an illness we can treat and against which we can vaccinate and employ protective measures to help the immunocompromised, elderly and very young.

But this approach, while more practical, must not encourage individual complacency. A majority of the population may contract some form of the virus, but it is not a prospect to cheerfully anticipate. Besides the diminishing but still-present morbidity and mortality, the

unresolved future repercussions of even trivial infections —
long COVID-19 — remain a concern for those who become
infected. We should still be careful how we live.

Right now, this makes decisions as routine as
attending the theater or eating in crowded restaurants
fraught with uncertainty. The government, which once
advised the public on what to do and how to live, appears
to have washed its hands of most responsibility and now
seems to be leaving decisions largely to the public. But
expert input would still be of immeasurable benefit in
helping us live our lives.

In what venues should we mask? When should we
test at home? What is the risk of attending a concert at
Soldier Field? Granted, there is no consensus, and the
recommendations will change over time, but we could still
use some advice from the medical community about the
COVID-19 risks of everyday life.

Meanwhile, there is certainly reason for optimism.
Antiviral drugs will get only better, and new vaccines are
being developed. A "universal" coronavirus vaccine could
provide protection against the constantly changing COVID-
19 variants. A nasal spray vaccine that induces high levels
of antibodies at the nose, the main portal of viral entry into
the body, might theoretically be safer and more effective
than the current vaccine booster regimen.

While we await those advances, there is no role for complacency by the public. Those officials charged with COVID-19 management must improve case tracking to include the results of home testing, coordinate national and global surveillance of COVID-19 variants, and facilitate wastewater surveillance of the virus, which can be an early indicator of a COVID-19 variant or a generalized outbreak.

At the same time, the government should encourage home testing, optimize the path from testing to delivery of oral COVID-19 medications, fund the development of more comfortable and durable protective masks, and push for better ventilation in residential buildings, businesses and schools.

As we continue the battle against COVID-19 into the third year, recall the eloquence of Winston Churchill as the tide was turning in World War II: "This is no time for boasts or glowing prophecies, but there is this — a year ago our position looked forlorn, and well-nigh desperate, to all eyes but our own. Today we may say aloud before an awe-struck world, 'We are still masters of our fate. We still are captain of our souls.'"

AIDS and COVID

Cory Franklin *Chicago Life* 7·1·22

In 1985, when I was directing the Cook County Hospital Medical Intensive Care Unit, we were caring for a greater number of AIDS patients than any hospital in the country outside of San Francisco or New York City. At one point, we were seeing 15% of all the AIDS patients in Chicago. The most common condition that brought AIDS patients to the ICU was a rare lung infection-*pneumocystis* pneumonia - and the survival of those patients in the ICU was dismal, prompting questions about whether they should be admitted to intensive care units. In many hospitals they weren't.

A decade later I was interviewed for a book about County Hospital called *Hospital* by Sydney Lewis. I recounted the most difficult administrative decision I ever made which concerned AIDS patients with pneumocystis pneumonia.

"Back in '86 we lost our first, roughly, ten AIDS patients who were in Intensive Care. One of the AIDS social workers, a very concerned young woman, said maybe we shouldn't be putting those people in Intensive Care. She felt we should do a hospice-type thing. Her argument was based on compassion: she didn't want to

see all these people suffer. And it was a seductive thing to say, 'Well, maybe we should do that.' But it was unprecedented, in my experience, to have a specific disease where you say that just because they have this disease, you don't put them in Intensive Care. I said to her, 'Give me another eighteen months (to see). And maybe it's a good thing to do, but I just don't know yet.' About three months later we had a survivor. Well, the moment you have one survivor, survival is not prohibitive and you now turn it into a much more complicated ethical question."

Within a year, we began to see more and more survivors. Certain patterns emerged and as they did, we learned better care. In the late 1980s we published our first paper on it, saying the mortality of this disease in the ICU was not prohibitive as everyone was documenting, it was actually only 50 to 60%. That's different. We were vilified. Every journal reviewer said, "You are making this up, this isn't our experience, this is terrible..."

Pessimism was rampant because it's easier to get your head around absolutes. The experts then moved the goalposts and said that even if the mortality in the ICU was improved, it didn't matter because those people would die shortly after leaving the hospital. But we did follow-up and found that at five years, 20% of our patients were still alive.

Not great survival, but these were people that most of the medical community gave up on and who would have died.

We turned out to be right – at least in the narrow sense. The lesson was that the field can change very quickly. Within a few years, prophylactic antibiotics could forestall or prevent pneumocystis pneumonia. Then came antiretroviral drugs that can render the AIDS virus quiescent for years. Today, there are very few AIDS patients with pneumocystis in the ICU, because the immune suppression is well-controlled. Many people go on to live long, full lives.

But in another sense, I realized we were wrong. If we used intensive care wisely, we could save people's lives – but what we could not do was change the course of the larger numbers of people with the disease. The effect the ICU had on the mortality of AIDS patients in the 1980s and early 1990s was negligible – the number of ICU AIDS survivors was simply too small to make a dent in the overall totals. It wasn't until later in the 1990s and the development of antiretroviral medications that the mortality of AIDS really did change and dwarfed our humble efforts.

Fast forward to the fall of 2020. In the first six months of the COVID pandemic - late winter, spring and early summer - COVID mortality in the US hovered between 5 and 6%. Gradually, by autumn, mortality had come down to under 2%. Any time that mortality of a condition comes down by two-thirds, something is happening. It might be a recording phenomenon – cases and deaths recorded differently, it might be change in the disease or the victims of the disease or it may be a care phenomenon (this was before vaccines were available, so that was not an issue). Usually, it is the result of a combination of the factors.

And now came medical experts, including some of the same people who pooh-poohed our efforts in the 1980s, saying exactly what I knew could not be - that the rapid drop in mortality was due to better care, primarily intensive care. Intensive care does not cause such a precipitous drop in so large a population so quickly, nevertheless it soon became the conventional wisdom that it did among epidemiologists, clinicians, public health authorities and journalists. When I asked journalists and doctors for some firm documentation rather than anecdotes to substantiate this, none was forthcoming.

At the beginning of the pandemic, clinicians employed ventilators for COVID pneumonia too liberally – and this *increased* mortality. Ventilators should only be used for a specific subset of COVID patients and can actually increase lung damage in some. This resulted in thousands of deaths worldwide before a learning curve developed. Paradoxically, when clinicians employed ventilators more judiciously, the mortality rate of COVID did drop. However in the face of hundreds of thousands of deaths, this effect was important but trivial, a raindrop in the ocean.

Soon, intensive care for COVID became better in other ways as well, and new drugs used in the intensive care unit definitely improved the prospects for those patients. But COVID patients in intensive care units are a small subset - fewer than 5% of all patients with the disease (now the percentage is even lower) and their mortality is still significant. The number saved is small in relation to the total numbers of COVID patients dying - most COVID deaths do not occur in the intensive care unit. For any single patient, chances of survival are much better than they were at the beginning of the pandemic. But in macro terms this was not the major factor accounting for the reduced mortality in the second half of 2020.

At best, the improvements in intensive care may have reduced overall mortality for all patients by perhaps 15%. This is certainly significant; the US has had more than one million deaths. This means 150,000 people may have been saved by intensive care during the two-plus years of the pandemic. But that works out to about four lives saved/day on average in every state in the country (Illinois has had more than 38,000 COVID deaths during the pandemic). The majority of the reduction in COVID mortality in the second half of 2020 was the primarily result of the evolution of less severe viral strains as well as fewer extremely susceptible hosts, many having died off in the first wave. Since 2021, the reduction in mortality is primarily due to vaccines.

The issue of how much benefit there is to various COVID interventions is not so much about whether they are effective, but how effective they really are. Intensive care, like masking, vaccinations, and social distancing, is an intervention that is effective to varying degrees against COVID. All these inventions work at the margins, and we must take care not to oversell their effect. It is possible that as we learn more, we may discover that some interventions don't work as well as we thought or do not justify the costs they entail.

In terms of vaccines, our best data today indicate that vaccines are quite effective at preventing serious illness, less so at preventing infection. Without question, vaccines have affected COVID mortality more than any other intervention and making better vaccines is one place to direct future efforts against COVID.

Considering masking, most low-tech masks are probably effective at preventing some droplet transmission (e.g. close contact coughs, sneezes) but do not do much to prevent fine aerosol transmission. In some situations, they are a reasonable preventive measure, but their use alone may minimize spread but will not eradicate COVID.

As I found out in the AIDS pandemic, intensive care for individual COVID patients can be lifesaving. But in terms of the overall pandemic death rates, it is not game changing. Like the other measures, it also works at the margins. But as we learned during the AIDS pandemic that's all we can hope for – any advantage we can find. Because until a gamechanger comes along, the efforts at the margins are what make all the difference.

Herd immunity against COVID-19 is unlikely. But we aren't powerless

Cory Franklin Robert A. Weinstein *Chicago Tribune*
7·25·22

"A man has got to know his limitations." That is one of the memorable phrases uttered by "Dirty Harry" Callahan, the fictional police inspector played by Clint Eastwood. Today, the world is learning its limitations in the ongoing COVID-19 pandemic, and the most important lesson is that a key strategy we banked on to defeat the virus — herd immunity — appears unobtainable.

Herd immunity is reached when enough people in a community acquire immunity to a disease, either through infection or vaccination or both, that it makes sustained transmission impossible and protects even those who are not immune. The strategy of mass vaccination campaigns to achieve herd immunity has worked well for childhood diseases such as diphtheria, which has essentially disappeared, and for other once-common diseases such as smallpox and polio. (The first U.S. case of polio in a decade was recently reported, thought to be brought in from outside the country.)

The percentage of people who must be immune to stop the spread of a disease depends primarily on how contagious the disease is. The commonly cited example is measles, which is extremely contagious and requires immunity in 90% to 95% of the population to halt transmission. In the past few years, measles outbreaks have occurred in the U.S. despite greater than 80% of the local population being vaccinated.

Which brings us to COVID-19. Early on, public health researchers and the World Health Organization estimated that a range of 60% to 70% population immunity would be necessary to control the disease. As the COVID-19 vaccines became available, more contagious variants also emerged. Public health experts were forced to move up the herd immunity estimate to 75% to 80%. But events on the ground have shattered that notion.

What went wrong with the herd immunity theory? In essence, two things. First, vaccine protection is incomplete and does not last long enough. Second, the virus is constantly mutating to circumvent vaccine protection.

The theory of herd immunity, like all scientific theories, depends on several assumptions, and these assumptions proved not to be true in real life. The first fallacy was that people who have acquired immunity would not acquire or pass on the disease; they must remain resistant. One year ago, after a July 4 gathering in Provincetown, Massachusetts, where nearly everyone was vaccinated, about 1,000 people came down with COVID-

19. That disproved the assumption that vaccinated individuals could not acquire or transmit COVID-19. We have since learned that vaccine-induced immunity wanes over time, thus prompting the need for booster shots, which themselves wane in effectiveness over time.

Second, herd immunity theory depends on immunity to a relatively stable disease. Measles does not change much from year to year, and the measles vaccine does not have to be reconfigured annually. In the first months of the COVID-19 pandemic, it was believed the virus would take a long time to mutate. But immune-evading variants appeared more quickly than expected in the U.S. and all over the world. Several countries with vaccination rates greater than 90%, such as Portugal, have experienced significant waves of infection this year, largely as a result of new variants.

Despite the failure to prevent all infections, vaccination has dramatically lessened the severity of disease and the number of COVID-19 deaths in most countries — no small achievement. This may represent a kind of "partial herd immunity," but the possibility of new variants and the limitations of the current vaccines represent a continuing worldwide threat.

As Dirty Harry said, we have our limitations — but we are not powerless. Work proceeds on a universal coronavirus vaccine and a nasal vaccine, both of which might be better suited to stopping COVID-19. We should increase our wastewater testing for COVID-19, which may provide a badly needed early-warning system for impending infection surges and new variants. Information technology can better integrate home testing with public reporting to prevent undercounts of cases, and this can also be used to facilitate quick drug treatment with Paxlovid for those who test positive.

A full-scale national evaluation of adequate indoor ventilation in our buildings, especially our schools, is overdue. When case counts are high, masking and social distancing in certain settings are a responsible way to protect the most vulnerable. Finally, because being overweight is such a strong risk factor for severe COVID-19, a national campaign to reduce obesity is in order. It worked for smoking.

In the near term, COVID-19 is not going away. We cannot say now whether it will be an ongoing significant health threat or a minor inconvenience. Realizing how little we control events, we must hope — with humility — that we are lucky, and it turns out to be the latter. But preparation is essential because, as baseball executive Branch Rickey observed, luck is the residue of design.

Or as Dirty Harry was fond of asking with menace, "Do you feel lucky?"

Here's how parents can meet the new school year with less anxiety

Cory Franklin Mary Hall *Chicago Tribune* 8·22·22

Fall may not yet be in the air, but school definitely is. Camps and family vacations are ending, and children are queuing up in pediatric waiting rooms, coming in for school and sports physicals, as well as for the inevitable minor injuries and illnesses of the summer. As children excitedly recount their summer activities and anticipate the upcoming school year with a mixture of hope and dread, another emotion permeates the pediatrician's office: courage.

Aristotle called courage the first of human qualities because it is "the quality which guarantees the others." Being a kid requires a modicum of courage every fall, for he or she is beginning something new. Some transitions are small — a new teacher — while others are dramatic — starting preschool, high school or a new job. From the child's view, the comforts of summer are past and every new beginning is fraught with at least some trepidation. Parents may treasure the first day of school with commemorative photos, but those photos often capture the uncertainty of young children or the annoyance of older ones.

As school begins, parents should summon courage as well. They place trust in teachers, classmates and fellow parents who will gradually become the child's community as the child becomes more independent. Uncertainties about whether the educational or social environment will be a good fit are accompanied by natural concerns about physical safety. Families do their best to optimize the situation for their children before sending them out like Alfred Tennyson's Light Brigade.

In the face of a new season of COVID-19, what can pediatricians, with their knowledge and experience with viral illnesses, vaccination, child development and mental health, do to support parents and children in helping them develop the requisite courage?

This fall, the stakes for children are high, especially because we have shortchanged their educational and social development in the last two years. School is important. Learning loss during the pandemic is well documented and is worse for many children in economically vulnerable circumstances and for those children with special needs. Social interactions are essential: Children have to see the faces of their friends and teachers, and they must be able to communicate easily and participate in extracurricular activities. Positive, age-appropriate social interactions help protect children from depression, anxiety and mental health disorders, which increased significantly during the previous two years.

Thankfully, COVID-19 remains a mild illness for most children. More than 75% have recovered from an infection one or more times. Although COVID- 19 infections have become more frequent with the newer variants, multisystem inflammatory syndrome, a serious condition seen in a small number of children early in the pandemic, has become much less common. This may be due to a combination of the variants being less severe and the childhood immunity wall developed through vaccination and natural infection.

As is true every year, children will get sick with colds this winter, and this will include COVID-19. With the knowledge that serious COVID-19 is becoming less widespread, especially in children, there are several actions that parents, teachers and administrators can take to optimize this school year for children by employing "the four As":

Accept the reality that viral illnesses are not only inevitable but necessary for building healthy immune systems in children.

Avoid, as much as possible, disruptions to children's schedules as we live through viral outbreaks this year. The immunity wall to COVID-19 is stronger now than at any time in the past, and we are better prepared for the virus than we were in 2020 or 2021. Barring any new developments, this should obviate the need for contact tracing, quarantines and lockdowns.

Allow children to experience the full range of social interactions, especially smiles, hugs, group activities, sports and field trips.

Assure children that the pandemic situation is improving and that optimism is warranted about the upcoming school year.

Children naturally spread germs when they are sick, but the adults around them are generally well protected through their own immune activation from frequent viral exposure. Recent literature suggests that adults who spend more time with young children tend to experience less severe COVID-19 illness compared with those who are not regularly exposed to children. When competing needs or risks exist, we should prioritize the needs of children if possible.

Nelson Mandela once said, "Courage is not the absence of fear, but the triumph over it. The brave man is not he who does not feel afraid, but he who conquers that fear." The next several months will be our crucible. COVID-19 outbreaks may occur even as we reconsider our responses to the improving circumstances.

As adults who love children, let's commit to grasping the nettle. We must screw up our courage so they can flourish in the ways they deserve.

The CDC knows better, but will it do better?

Cory Franklin Robert A. Weinstein *Chicago Tribune*
8·25·22

The Centers for Disease Control and Prevention has performed poorly during the COVID-19 pandemic, and CDC Director Rochelle Walensky promises wholesale changes in the agency. She publicly admits, "We are responsible for some pretty dramatic, pretty public mistakes, from testing to data to communications."

That is a welcome and rare degree of candor from a public official in the face of public malfunction, but her promised reorganization will not necessarily guarantee a better response to future pandemics. A larger budget and bigger workforce are likely, and these alone do not automatically make for a more effective organization. To address the inevitable pandemics of the future, here are six things a reconfigured CDC should do:

Clarify the role of medicine versus public health during an outbreak. A major problem during COVID-19 was the blurred line between medicine and public health. There is inherent overlap, but the role of public health in a pandemic is to identify the problem's scope through means such as testing, then recommend control measures. The role of medical doctors is diagnosis and treatment of infected patients. The CDC should clarify these two roles, which became confused during COVID-19.

Refocus on infectious diseases. The CDC was founded in 1946 to combat malaria, then endemic in the Southeast U.S. Domestic malaria was soon effectively eradicated, and the agency's mission expanded to fight other infectious diseases including polio, rabies, tuberculosis, smallpox and rubella. While the CDC has been quite successful in controlling these diseases and some noncommunicable problems such as cancer clusters and lead poisoning, this success has not transferred over to noninfectious conditions such as obesity and gun violence. The COVID-19 failures suggest a needed return to and redoubling of efforts in addressing serious infectious disease outbreaks.

Have its place identified in the chain of command during outbreaks. The CDC is an investigative and advisory agency, not a rule-making regulatory body. There was a problem during the pandemic with its relationship to other health agencies and personnel: National Institutes of Health, Food and Drug Administration, the U.S. Department of Health and Human Services, surgeon general and state health departments. A pandemic requires strict lines of authority. During World War II's Manhattan Project, when the atomic bomb was developed, one individual, Leslie Groves, was responsible for every facet of the program. His expertise was neither scientific nor technical, but coming from the military, he was adept at management and organizational control. The White House should name this type of individual above all agencies, with primary responsibility during future outbreaks, who can delineate the exact role of the CDC in relation to the other organizations in pandemic control.

Improve surveillance of outbreaks. Surveillance is key to public health. The CDC came late to the realization of community transmission from asymptomatic or mildly symptomatic people and underestimated the importance of adequate indoor ventilation. An essential part of a CDC restructuring should be the early identification of outbreaks and how and where they spread. Because wastewater surveillance, using new molecular identification, has proved effective in isolating the location of new COVID-19 variants, the CDC should consider an expanded national wastewater surveillance program.

Improve information technology. In a new outbreak, astute clinicians usually identify the initial cases, but with supercomputers and tech companies such as Google, Apple and Microsoft at its disposal, the CDC can institute a rapid early warning system. It should have the capability of incorporating into its databases the results of home testing, an emerging feature of pandemic management. Outside experts from other disciplines such as finance, adept at identifying complex trends, may be valuable serving as consultants.

Employ honest communication. Public communication by the CDC has been disastrous during COVID-19. Some mistakes are being repeated with monkeypox. (Alarm spread among the broad public about a disease with fairly discrete risk factors, while those most at risk — including men who have sex with men — were not informed effectively.) Messaging should be understandable, simple and direct and include what is known and what is not known about an outbreak. No agency should withhold information out of fear the public will misuse it. If and when that happens, it's usually because officials bungled the crafting or delivery of the message.

There is a place for political considerations in public health messaging, but ideology should never compromise clear communication. To inform journalists and the public, the CDC should consider employing messaging specialists from outside medicine. Finally, and this is crucial, the CDC should listen to and not suppress dissenting voices, who turned out to be right on some COVID-19 issues. Where all think alike, no one thinks very much.

Plenty of actors besides the CDC deserve blame. Two major operational models of American medicine were ineffective. Walensky admitted the CDC became too attached to the academic model of teaching and university-associated hospitals, where publishing studies in medical journals — a long, arduous process — was prioritized over managing a rapid disease outbreak. Likewise, large hospital networks, where profit is the goal, did no better than the academic model in dealing with a public health emergency.

A Yoruban proverb says that yesterday's truth is often tomorrow's folly. COVID-19 has demonstrated that much of what we believed in early 2020, we now know was wrong. This should prompt the entire American medical community to do what the CDC is doing: reexamine its beliefs and deployment of its resources before the next pandemic arrives.

Missed opportunities from COVID-19

Cory Franklin Robert A. Weinstein *Chicago Tribune*
9·14·22

With two-and-a-half years of COVID-19 experience
behind us, we can now identify the missed opportunities
the medical and public health communities had to control
the pandemic. There are three well-established areas where
the virus caught the world unprepared: asymptomatic viral
transmission from the infected to the uninfected; airborne
spread from extremely small particles, especially indoors;
and rapid emergence of new COVID-19 variants. These
unexpected and mostly unprecedented developments
thwarted early efforts to control the virus and caused
devastating consequences including more than 6.5 million
deaths worldwide and counting.

- **Asymptomatic transmission:** With its initial
  community spread, COVID-19 appeared to behave like
  influenza in early 2020. Gradually a crucial difference
  between COVID-19 and the flu became apparent. With
  the flu, the majority of the population has been exposed
  in previous years to some flu variant, so an immune
  response and the attendant symptoms — fever, sore
  throat, runny nose — develop quickly with subsequent
  infections. So, as the flu virus becomes transmissible,
  many people are already exhibiting symptoms.

What was unrecognized with COVID-19 was that many infected patients could transmit the virus before showing symptoms. Because this was a new virus that no one had experienced in the past, humans did not have specific immune memory. As a result, those infected did not show symptoms right away. Before people knew they were sick, they were becoming contagious as the virus multiplied in their bodies. The situation is different today because most people have had COVID-19 or have been vaccinated. With that acquired immune memory, they develop symptoms earlier, and those symptoms correlate more closely, but not perfectly, with the potential for viral transmission.

In the early days of COVID-19, the implications of asymptomatic transmission were profound. Initial claims were that better testing and contact tracing in the first phase of the pandemic would have limited COVID- 19 spread. In retrospect, asymptomatic transmission made that unlikely. If you can't see obvious symptoms indicating that certain people are infected, whom do you choose to test? And until you have some positive test results, how do you contact-trace? (In truth, billions of dollars were spent on contact tracing with little to show for it.)

In the first months, leaders in charge of pandemic control failed to adequately warn people to avoid crowd gatherings and public transportation, where infected but asymptomatic people were likely to come together. Additionally, conflicting advice from public health officials about wearing masks perplexed Americans. Surgical masks offer some protection against certain forms of transmission, and well-fitting, respirator-grade masks provide strong protection. But months went by before officials settled on that messaging. As a result, untold thousands of people confused about mask-wearing acquired infections. Some confusion continues to this day.

- **Airborne spread from extremely small particles (aerosols):** Most traditional respiratory viral infections are spread by larger particles that travel limited distances. Infection is caused by close contact between two people, or when larger particles land on surfaces or on someone's hands and become sources for infection. This was the early message put out by experts for COVID-19. In March 2020, the World Health Organization stated unequivocally (with "not" in caps), "COVID-19 is NOT airborne. The coronavirus is mainly transmitted through droplets generated when an infected person coughs, sneezes or speaks."

In fact, COVID-19 was then and today is often airborne. (Keep reading.) Countries including the U.S. were slow to recover from this serious scientific miscalculation and faulty declaration. The dominant narrative resulted in an overemphasis in measures such as disinfecting surfaces and avoiding touching the mouth, nose and eyes. To date, it is unlikely anyone has caught COVID-19 from handling the mail. But this emphasis came at the expense of attention to indoor air quality. Now we know that airborne spread by much smaller particles is common and possibly the most important mode of transmission in many settings. The WHO was loath to emphasize aerosol transmission for two years.

Failure to appreciate the potential danger of these aerosol particles from the breath of an infected person meant the public was unaware that transmission indoors was far more likely than outdoors. (In the summer of 2020, Chicago inexplicably closed parks and beaches, but not the bars.) Reducing the time we spend indoors with others and improving indoor ventilation, especially in schools where open windows and frequent outdoor breaks should be routine, received insufficient emphasis. Even today, government officials give insufficient attention to improving indoor ventilation. Aerosol scientists should be key scientific advisers.

- **Rapid emergence of variants:** While some virologists warned early on about the ability of the

COVID-19 virus to mutate, most of the early scientific literature downplayed how rapidly this could occur. Newer viral identification techniques were essential to revealing that variants appeared much more quickly than anticipated, surprising much of the public health community, which had banked on vaccination and herd immunity to stop the pandemic. Variants reduced vaccine effectiveness and essentially put an end to the early herd-immunity strategy. Most important, new COVID-19 variants pose a recurring problem, limiting vaccine durability.

For future reference: Confronting a rapidly expanding pandemic requires using forward thinking, expecting the unexpected and, above all, employing a flexible approach when the facts no longer conform to our beliefs.

As George Bernard Shaw once observed, "Those who cannot change their minds cannot change anything."

Is the COVID-19 pandemic really over?

Cory Franklin Robert A. Weinstein *Chicago Tribune*
10·4·22

Joe Biden elucidated his thoughts on the status of the COVID-19 pandemic in an interview with "60 Minutes" last month. "The pandemic is over. ... We still have a problem with COVID. We're still doing a lot of work on it. But the pandemic is over. If you notice, no one's wearing masks. Everybody seems to be in pretty good shape, and so, I think it's changing."

Leaving aside for a moment whether the pandemic is indeed over, a breakdown of that statement reveals some truth — the pandemic is changing — and some fiction — not everyone is in pretty good shape, and there are some problematic consequences. And whether to wear masks? That is a complicated question.

While the pandemic is in a different phase than it was two-and-a-half years ago, to call it "over" displays a level of optimism that intrudes on certain facts. The U.S. will experience more than 250,000 COVID-19 deaths this year, based on how numbers are trending, fewer than in the previous two years but still a considerable number. That number is front-weighted — there were more deaths in the first half of the year than there will be in the second half — but even in the second half of 2022, American death totals from COVID-19 will approach the 58,000 of the 10-year Vietnam War.

There is another alarming factor to consider: overall excess deaths from all causes. In other words, how many people died in excess of the number who would have died in a typical year? This metric continues to rise, not only in the U.S. but in most European and Asian countries. The expected pattern following most pandemics is for excess deaths in a region to fall, presumably because the sickest people died during the pandemic, but this is not what is happening now.

No one is sure why excess deaths are increasing, but it is likely the result of several factors: consequences of previous COVID-19 infection, notably blood clots and heart problems; underappreciated social chaos of the pandemic, such as homicides, suicides, alcoholism and drugs; and the strain on the healthcare system resulting in delayed diagnoses and responses to serious and ultimately fatal conditions that have no connection to COVID-19. Whatever the causes, the abundance of excess deaths has not shown signs of going away, and American life expectancy continues to decline, a reversal of a century-old pattern.

Equally disturbing are the consequences of long COVID-19, the health problems patients experience for months after contracting COVID-19. These difficulties can occur even after a trivial COVID-19 infection. According to the Centers for Disease Control and Prevention: "Older adults are less likely to have long COVID than younger adults. Nearly three times as many adults ages 50-59 currently have long COVID than those age 80 and older." Especially concerning is a new report published by the prestigious science journal *Nature*. In a survey of more than 150,000 veterans, at one year after COVID-19 infection, there was a notable increase in neurological and musculoskeletal problems including strokes, cognition and memory disorders, and new mental health disability.

As the president noted, fewer people are wearing masks now. Based on declining case numbers nationwide, the CDC recently downgraded its recommended infection control measures, including stepping back from the mandatory use of face masks in healthcare facilities. The CDC now says facilities in regions without high transmission can "choose not to require" all doctors, patients and visitors to mask. Many disagree with those recommendations and continue to enforce mask mandates.

Hospitals and clinics are obviously a special situation. They are high-risk locations, and while those who work there may not need to mask where there are no patients, such as in staff meeting rooms and lobbies, it seems intuitively obvious that in certain areas such as chemotherapy units, wearing masks remains a sensible transmission precaution. Others at increased risk of serious COVID-19 illness may benefit from masking in crowded indoor settings.

Biden first declared independence from the pandemic on July 4, 2021, even as a delta variant surge was emerging that would end in more than 150,000 cases and 2,000 deaths per day by the end of that summer. President Donald Trump's earlier predictions about the pandemic going away met with an equally unsuccessful outcome.

Rather than listen to presidents, we would do better to refer the question to one of cinema's great academic thinkers from the 1978 movie *Animal House* — John "Bluto" Blutarsky, played by John Belushi. Sure, Bluto's Faber College GPA was an unimpressive 0.0, but don't let that fool you. He knew what he was talking when he said, "Over? Did you say 'over'? Nothing is over until we decide it is."

The key to unlocking the mysteries of COVID-19 is understanding immunity

Cory Franklin *Chicago Tribune* 10·24·22

Among the many medical puzzles about COVID-19 that continue to confound experts: Why does one spouse contract COVID-19 while in many cases the other does not? Why does the African continent have far fewer COVID-19 cases and deaths per capita than the other continents? Why does Singapore have more COVID-19 cases per capita than the U.S. but less than one-tenth the per capita death rate? What protects better from future COVID-19 infection, previous infection or vaccination?

Some of the partial answers to these questions are obvious: In terms of prevention, both previous infection and vaccination protect better than either alone. Environmental factors and mitigation efforts play a role in how the virus spreads, while age, obesity and underlying health affect COVID-19's severity. The novel characteristics of the virus and its variants — transmissibility and lethality — surely matter, as does chance, which invariably exerts itself in most medical mysteries.

But the real key to demystifying the COVID-19 pandemic is immunity — explaining why some individuals are able to resist infection, while others are susceptible, and still others are especially vulnerable. Unfortunately, even our best immunologists have little more than a rudimentary understanding of how immunity in COVID-19 works.

Immunity is basically how the body defends itself from germs, and it is a complicated phenomenon. We are born with certain types of immunity; we acquire some immunity through vaccination and some is developed through exposure to various infectious agents. One theory about why Africa has been relatively protected from COVID-19 is the outdoor population's greater exposure to germs — the so-called hygiene hypothesis. The lower mortality from COVID-19 in East Asia may be the result of contact with earlier COVID- 19-related coronaviruses in these countries, which would have conferred some protective immunity.

Some of our immunity is the result of producing antibodies to specific diseases. But immunity goes beyond that. While antibody levels in the blood can be measured, they do not always correlate well with whatever protection our immune systems actually deliver. Besides antibodies, certain white blood cells generate a different form of immunity. Also, there is a local immunity — the respiratory airways and gastrointestinal tract have cells designed to keep hostile invaders out. The interaction among all these components is extremely complex — like the pieces on a chessboard in the hands of a grandmaster.

A recent study published in the journal *Nature* gave an indication of how important immunity is during pandemics. The Black Death, caused by a specific plague bacterium, may have killed as many as 200 million people in Afro-Eurasia during the Middle Ages. It is the single greatest mortality event in human history. The *Nature* study analyzed the DNA of centuries-old skeletons and found that those with a certain genetic mutation were 40% more likely to survive the plague than other people were. That particular gene was essential to making proteins that primed the immune system to recognize the lethal plague bacterium. The study said, "Clarifying the dynamics that have shaped the human immune system is key to understanding how historical diseases contributed to disease susceptibility today."

It is humbling to think that our descendants will pass on mutations for centuries that may help people survive future COVID-19. From a historical scientific standpoint, we are basically in the same primitive spot in medicine that we were in physics before quantum mechanics revolutionized the field. In the early years of the 20th century, Nobel laureate physicists J.J. Thomson and Ernest Rutherford proposed simple models of the atom based on the physics of Isaac Newton. Less than 20 years later, another Nobel laureate, Niels Bohr, changed physics forever with the Bohr atomic model, based on early quantum mechanics rather than classical Newtonian physics. While extremely complicated, the practical effects of the Bohr model, now obsolete itself, are evident in the development of atomic power and (regrettably) atomic weapons. Perhaps even more important was how quantum mechanics changed thinking about physics, science and the world in general.

Discovering the secrets of immunity and the reasons people respond to infections as they do will open up new vistas in medicine just as quantum mechanics did in physics. It will also guide us toward practical answers about the pandemic, including who benefits most from vaccination, which groups need the greatest protection, and what measures are likely to be effective in enhancing personal immunity. Some of what seems inexplicable today will one day be understandable.

Since biblical times, contagions have struck some humans while passing over others in ways we do not understand. When the final account of the COVID- 19 pandemic is written, it will be the story of the essential trait of disease immunity.

COVID-19 will cause long-term devastation to our society on many fronts

Cory Franklin Robert A. Weinstein *Chicago Tribune*
11·8·22

Halloween is over; Christmas beckons. "Monster Mash" is out; "All I Want for Christmas Is You" is in. Feel-good movies have replaced seasonal zombie and vampire flicks. In the U.S., our real-life zombie movie is called COVID- 19, and it has caused more than one million deaths. Along with that, there have been hundreds of thousands of non-COVID-19 excess deaths, and the number of people with long-term disabilities from COVID-19 may top off at a million or more. But no zombie apocalypse movie could imagine the profound long-term devastation COVID-19 might eventually do to American society on so many fronts.

The most immediate COVID-19 effect has been on K-12 education. In a trend that is unlikely to reverse anytime soon, math and reading scores for fourth and eighth graders have declined significantly in nearly every state, coincident with the pandemic. High school students also had falling ACT scores, exacerbating a decline that predated the pandemic. Deterioration in academic performance has been most dramatic in children who were performing poorly before COVID-19. The implications for

199

American competitiveness are obvious, and we are reinforcing a two-tier educational system. An overhaul of our teaching methods, remote and in-person, should be a top national priority.

The American economy appears to be rebounding somewhat from the economic shock of the first two years of the pandemic, but adjusted consumer prices are at their highest level in 40 years, the result of a number of factors, some of which are clearly pandemic-related. The current inflation rate is between 8% and 9%, and while the outcome of the inflationary pressure is impossible to predict, there is a chance the economy could be crippled for the rest of this decade.

An even bigger unknown is the social effects of the pandemic. In 2020, physician and sociologist Nicholas Christakis wrote a book, *Apollo's Arrow*, drawing on past pandemics, some of which radically upended the social order of their times. It is a clarion call of how much can change as the result of disease.

In the 14th century, bubonic plague, also known as the Black Death, killed more than 20 million people in Europe, one-third of the continent's population. This essentially ended feudalism on the continent; the large number of deaths created a severe labor shortage, and surviving serfs were able seek higher wages than they could earn working for their lords. Without people to work the great manors, owning land was no longer a source of extreme wealth, and this precipitated a dramatic migration to urban centers. This, in turn, bred a new era of disorder.

Christakis quotes the observations of Italian chronicler Agnolo di Tura as the plague waned, "And then, when the pestilence abated, all who survived gave themselves over to pleasures: monks, priests, nuns, and laymen and women all enjoyed themselves, and none worries about spending and gambling. And everyone thought himself rich because he had escaped and regained the world, and no one knew how to allow himself to do nothing."

An even greater upheaval occurred in the 16th century in what is now Mexico when smallpox, an extremely contagious disease brought by European ships, ravaged the Aztec empire. Smallpox was critical to the Spanish conquest of much of Mesoamerica. When the Spanish conquistador Hernán Cortés and his troops marched on the Aztec capital in 1519 to subdue the city, they were completely outnumbered. But through superior weaponry, astute generalship and alliance with some of the smaller tribes, Cortés managed to hold off the Aztecs until the natives were subdued in large measure because of the smallpox epidemic. With little immunity, 90% of the Aztec nation succumbed to the disease. Demoralized survivors were incapacitated and, in their last stand, unable to resist the Spanish. The final blow to the Aztec empire and much of the Indigenous population may have been widespread famine, caused by too few people to care for the crops.

In a primarily agrarian economy such as that of the Aztecs or feudal Europe, a pandemic can be absolutely devastating. With the 21st century technology available to us, we have a more resilient society — the worst will not necessarily occur. You can now order online at your favorite restaurant and work from home in your underwear via virtual meetings. But will these innovations be scant consolation if the educational, economic and social consequences of COVID-19 tear at the fabric of the country?

So far, the world has not ended; perhaps COVID-19 is a wake-up call. But the looming educational, economic and social threats must be taken seriously. The Rev. Martin Luther King Jr. once said, "We are not makers of history. We are made by history." As such, we must be diligent to avoid becoming the Aztecs or the cast of a zombie apocalypse movie.

American children need a higher-quality science education

Cory Franklin Robert A. Weinstein *Chicago Tribune*
11·30·22

One of the most devastating effects of the COVID-19 pandemic has been the debt it has created, a debt that we owe our kids that will be hard ever to pay back. In the past three years, much of what has occurred — school closings, lockdowns, remote learning — whether warranted or not, has had a profound academic and social effect on children, adolescents and young adults. We have an obligation to repay them.

The depressing data from the National Assessment of Education Progress demonstrates dramatic declines in reading and math scores in American grade schoolers, with students from poorer schools showing the worst declines, perpetuating an unequal two-tiered system. The quality of science education was not measured, but scientific illiteracy has been a persistent problem in American schools for decades. There is much science to be learned in the face of the pandemic, and this is a wide-ranging opportunity to improve the situation.

One way to do so is by constructing age-appropriate school curricula, taking what we have learned from COVID-19 and teaching schoolchildren about germs, hygiene, vaccines and immunity. Just as important, we must remove some of the fear of their environment that we have inculcated in them.

For the youngest children in kindergarten through third grade, the most important lesson is to teach them what germs are and that germs are a natural part of our environment not to be feared because although some can cause disease, germs are usually harmless, sometimes even beneficial. Moreover, the best way to prevent the spread of germs is by practicing good hand hygiene and cough etiquette: how to wash hands without ritualizing the activity (teachers should continually demonstrate proper technique) and how to cover the mouth and nose when coughing or sneezing.

Middle schoolers should learn that germs are specifically viruses and bacteria, identifying the differences between the two and how they both cause infection. All viruses and bacteria are not the same: The virus that causes measles is different from the virus that causes influenza. While schools should teach which germs cause specific diseases, the emphasis should again be on reassuring students that most viruses and bacteria are benign. Students generally have nothing to fear from them in their daily lives as long as they adhere to basic hygiene principles.

By junior high, students are sophisticated enough to learn more about how germs cause disease, whether by the air, droplets from coughs and sneezes or contaminated surfaces. They can be made aware that some diseases like influenza are seasonal and others are endemic to specific regions of the world, such as malaria in tropical climates. This is a good time to impart medical successes including the amazing story of one of the 20th century's great discoveries, penicillin, which was discovered by serendipity when a mold traveled through an open window and landed on a petri dish. They can also learn how scientists' heroic efforts essentially eradicated diseases such as smallpox and puerperal fever. They can hear the stories of famous historical men and women such as Florence Nightingale and Ignaz Semmelweis, both of whom battled an entrenched medical establishment.

High school students are ready for more advanced issues such as how vaccines work and an introduction to human immunity, a critical factor in understanding the primary defense against germs. This is also where students can learn about subjects such as the relative effectiveness of lockdowns and masking in different settings and how those questions are studied. It is obvious that high school students should also be educated about the viruses and bacteria that cause diseases that are spread through sex — and how to prevent them.

Besides instructing our youth, the primary goal of an education campaign should be to allay the fear of infections, much of which has been instilled in children during the pandemic. Part of this involves confronting controversies. When asked about teaching and discussion around COVID-19 in school, the 9-year-old grandchild of one of us said, "I think they avoid it because it is too political." This is untenable; it should be possible to discuss the issues without having the lessons devolve into Democrat versus Republican, but this means intellectually honest, nonpartisan lessons and instructors.

In the New Testament, it is written, "Suffer little children, and forbid them not, to come unto me: for of such is the kingdom of Heaven." This biblical message is that the future belongs to children, and our obligation is to guide them. The COVID-19 pandemic offers a teachable moment to inform, educate and, most important, reassure them: There is a safe path forward, and they can make sense of the chaos in the world that we have created.

As we enter the peak of the respiratory virus season, parents should be prudent

Cory Franklin Mary Hall *Chicago Tribune* 12·15·22

Over thousands of years, viruses and humans have evolved together. The spread of viruses is a basic feature of nature, and it is an immutable fact that controlling nature is difficult, but not always impossible. In this respect, notable human accomplishments include agriculture, sanitation, hydroelectric power, vaccines and aviation. Those, however, are exceptions. More often, attempts to control nature are either extremely limited in success or result in outright failure. Even when successful, the process is long and arduous and often results in tragic missteps. Before aviation became routine with the control of gravity, thousands of passengers and pilots died in plane crashes.

More successful than our attempts at controlling nature has been our ability to accommodate and coexist with it. When it comes to respiratory viruses, children are especially adept at this. Their immune systems are designed to respond immediately and efficiently to viruses they confront for the first time. This is probably why, in the case of COVID-19, they were less likely to get sick than adults, for whom the virus was also a new encounter.

For various reasons, there was very little spread of respiratory viruses for the first two years of the pandemic.

Those viruses are spreading now, and children have some catching up to do in their response to the viruses in their environment owing to unusually low viral exposure in 2020 and 2021. Fortunately, kids are well adapted to manage this catch-up process, and the annoyance of them suffering through a seemingly interminable series of viruses actually means we are well on our way through this process.

What can parents do in the face of the likelihood their children will get sick this winter? The primary goal is to help children feel better when they get colds or respiratory infections. This includes providing physical and emotional comfort and knowing the warning signs of when something more serious can be developing. This is admittedly not always easy because when kids are sick, they are uncomfortable. Parents, sensing that discomfort, will understandably be distressed.

Take heart, this is not all bad: From the standpoint of the child's immune system, a viral infection is a balancing act. It is frightening to have a virus overwhelm the immune system, but this is a rare occurrence. At the same time, the child's body is learning how to fight that virus more effectively, preparing for the next round.

Another parental responsibility is teaching kids not to spread viruses. This means using good manners such as washing hands and coughing into elbows. Have children stay home from school when they are sick. But remember that the spread of viruses is inevitable, especially with children. Kids will always catch colds from other kids, and the best parents can do is cut down on the frequency of transmission. By allowing youngsters to participate in normal activities, parents are actually helping kids — even with the awareness the children will sometimes be exposed — because those illnesses make the body stronger and healthier. Keep in mind that once the child has recovered, his or her body will have learned something new about that virus and as a result fortified its defenses.

Parents can also be proactive by helping kids keep their bodies healthy, so they are well prepared if and when they do get a viral illness. This includes reminding children to eat healthy foods and get exercise and enough sleep. For their mental health, minimize screen time. No good will come from long hours with cellphones, iPads, computers or the television.

In winter 2020 at the onset of the COVID-19 pandemic, responses of the government and medical community were designed to protect older and sicker people, who were the primary victims of COVID-19. Inadvertently, these measures did much to hurt children physically, mentally, socially and developmentally. The virus was extremely contagious, and there were many things we didn't know about COVID-19, including the fact that children were at much lower risk of severe illness. Much of the harm was done in an attempt to control nature and stop COVID-19 completely, which in this case turned out to be a fool's errand as mainland China is now discovering to its chagrin.

Authorities may have overstepped in trying to protect our children from harm over the past three years, but parents can right the situation going forward. Be prudent. Protect your children from the slings and arrows of this season's respiratory viruses — but don't overprotect them. Their immune systems are resilient, and in virtually every case, the children will recover and be stronger for it. Pay as much attention to their mental and emotional health as you do to their physical well-being — in fact, maybe more, because those aspects are fragile and parents can do much to be a positive influence.

Love is as important as any medication — that is one way you can control nature.

US COVID-19 deaths are still high, but let's learn from forecasters' mistakes

Cory Franklin Robert A. Weinstein *Chicago Tribune* 1·3·23

In a recent NFL game, the Indianapolis Colts led the Minnesota Vikings 33-0 at halftime. At that point, Las Vegas was offering odds better than 100-1 the Colts would win, but the Vikings staged a furious second-half rally and won on a field goal in overtime. It was one of the biggest comebacks in NFL history and proved once again that it is not always possible to predict the outcome of an event before it ends.

The same is true of the COVID-19 pandemic as it enters its fourth year. In May 2020, *Business Insider* CEO Henry Blodget and journalist David Plotz wrote, "Back in January, the United States and South Korea each identified their first confirmed coronavirus case on the same day. South Korea responded immediately and competently, by testing, tracing, and isolating cases and getting ahead of the epidemic. The United States ... never marshaled the strong federal response that could have slowed the outbreak before it really got rolling. Three months later ... South Korea is close to exterminating the virus."

In early 2021, Pulitzer Prize-winning science writer Lawrence Wright critiqued the U.S. COVID-19 response: "We did the worst job in the world." Blodget, Plotz and

Wright were merely echoing common sentiments of many medical observers that the U.S. had controlled COVID-19 less capably than any other country.

That was then; this is now. According to Worldometer, an independent website that has provided COVID-19 statistics throughout the pandemic, at least 30 and possibly as many as 50 industrialized countries have had more COVID-19 cases per capita than the U.S. has had. (The number depends on whether small island nations are included.)

As 2020 ended, the U.S. accounted for 25% of the world's COVID-19 cases. Now it accounts for just over 15%, and the fraction is dropping steadily. Some countries that were initially lauded for their COVID-19 response — Singapore, New Zealand and Czechia — have long since passed the U.S. in cases per capita. And South Korea, which was supposedly close to exterminating the virus? Overall cases per capita are now higher than in the U.S. South Korea currently has one of the highest case totals in the world.

There are some important caveats. This data includes officially reported cases and doesn't include many cases identified by home testing or those never reported to public health officials. So while there are more cases in the U.S. than the Worldometer numbers report, there is no indication the U.S. underreports cases disproportionately compared with other countries.

This should not be taken as evidence the U.S. has improved its response dramatically; rather, the newer variants have obviously caught up with other countries. Omicron and subsequent variants have overwhelmed many countries least affected in 2020, despite their policies of social distancing, vaccination and masking.

Since the fall, Japan has had the highest absolute case total in the world. In the first year of the pandemic, Japan had a quarter of a million cumulative cases; it now has more than 100 times that number. Unfortunately, the U.S. trend line of deaths per capita isn't falling as dramatically as the trend line for total cases. The U.S. is currently 16th in the world in deaths per capita and moving up, behind only Peru and countries in Eastern Europe. For comparison: Deaths and mortality, which is total deaths divided by total cases, are dropping in the U.S. but much slower than in the rest of the world. In addition, according to a study in the journal *Nature*, during the pandemic the U.S. has had one of the world's highest rates of excess deaths — that is, the number of observed deaths from all causes beyond the expected number if the pandemic had not occurred.

There is no obvious reason U.S. mortality and deaths per capita are higher here than in most of the world.

It has little or nothing to do with the varying quality of medical care globally, as some postulated early in the pandemic. Vaccination rates are probably a partial reason — the U.S. rate is lower than in many industrialized countries — but overall, U.S. vaccination rates are higher than those of many countries with lower death rates and lower mortality rates.

The major reason U.S. death rates are comparatively high is probably the high number of high-risk, susceptible patients in its population — a relatively higher percentage of patients who are elderly, obese or immunocompromised than in most other countries. Regardless of the caustic criticism leveled by many science journalists and medical experts, we can't remake the nation's demography. Yes, giving booster shots to high-risk individuals will improve things but will not solve the problem.

Expert predictions do not always age well. In July, Dr. Eric Feigl-Ding, one of the world's most cited public health experts, predicted the United Kingdom could see 60,000 monkeypox cases per day by the end of 2022. Yet in one recent week, there were five total cases and official reporting in the U.K. has stopped due to low case numbers.

Clearly, there are forces at work that no one can understand completely. As bettors cocksure the Colts would trounce the Vikings could have told you.

For all the good Dr. Fauci did at the NIH, he should have exited the stage sooner

Cory Franklin *Chicago Tribune* 1·19·23

Dr. Anthony Fauci, who began his career at the National Institutes of Health during Lyndon Johnson's administration, has stepped down as director of the National Institute of Allergy and Infectious Diseases and chief medical adviser to President Joe Biden. To put it in perspective, after more than five decades of distinguished and controversial government service, his legacy will be bittersweet — not quite the hero his supporters lionize or the villain his detractors portray.

Judged by his medical record alone, Fauci is in the top echelon of American physicians. He did groundbreaking work in immunology and helped develop lifesaving drugs for serious rheumatologic diseases. He discovered how to re-dose certain cancer drugs, turning a 98% mortality rate for one disease into a 93% remission rate. His honors include a Lasker Award, the highest award in biomedical science other than the Nobel Prize, and the Presidential Medal of Freedom, the highest civilian award in the United States, given to him by President George W. Bush in 2008.

But there is more to the story. F. Scott Fitzgerald famously observed, "There are no second acts in American life," but Fauci did have a second act when he switched specialties from immunology to infectious diseases just before HIV/AIDS began to sweep the world. By virtue of his government position, Fauci became the U.S. point person for the global HIV epidemic.

His early efforts were criticized by the gay community for the government's tentative initial response to the crisis and the sluggish pace of drug development for HIV. Fauci's harshest critic was prominent activist and gay rights advocate Larry Kramer, who castigated Fauci publicly and went so far as to call him a "murderer."

Fauci didn't retort, and eventually he and Kramer became friends, working together to revolutionize government drug trials and increase patients' access to experimental drugs. Ultimately, it was for his work in AIDS relief that Fauci received the Presidential Medal of Freedom. When COVID-19 hit in 2020, Fauci had been with the NIH for more than 50 years, and he became the government's chief medical spokesperson for the pandemic. He had to walk back some of his early pronouncements on de-emphasizing masks and predicting herd immunity.

He was an advocate of aggressive lockdown measures, which infuriated conservative politicians who anticipated the resulting damage to commerce and children's education. Elon Musk recently tweeted, "My pronouns are Prosecute/Fauci."

Much of this criticism is unfair and unwarranted. Many of Fauci's early statements arose from uncertainties in the first stages of the pandemic. However, none of this absolves Fauci from the most serious charges against him as pandemic spokesperson, which include suppressing dissent from the Great Barrington Declaration and a disturbing reticence to candidly discuss gain-of-function research.

Fauci and his superior, Dr. Francis Collins, director of the National Institutes of Health, colluded to silence three prominent scientists — Harvard University's Martin Kulldorff, Oxford University's Sunetra Gupta and Stanford University's Jay Bhattacharya — who issued the Great Barrington Declaration, a proposal to end large-scale lockdowns in favor of focused protection of high-risk populations, such as the elderly.

In an email to Fauci, Collins wrote: "This proposal from the three fringe public health researchers ... seems to be getting a lot of attention — and even a co-signature from Nobel Prize winner Mike Leavitt at Stanford. There needs to be a quick and devastating published take down of its premises. ... Is it underway?" Fauci complied willingly, the Great Barrington Declaration was publicly trashed and its otherwise respected signatories became pariahs in academic circles.

Whether right or wrong, the Great Barrington Declaration would have stimulated public debate and greater scientific analysis of the pandemic, which was badly lacking. Fauci has been quoted as "representing science," but it is anti-science to silence dissenting opinions and attack other scientists who are acting in good faith. Likewise, gain-of-function research, in which viruses are manipulated to adopt new characteristics, may have played a role in the origin of COVID-19. Such research occurs in China, and Fauci is one of the few people in the world knowledgeable enough to explain its potential benefits and dangers. For whatever reason, with all the interviews Fauci does, he rarely, if ever, alludes to it and has never explained the subject in depth to the public.

In the final analysis, Fauci's biggest failing was not exiting the stage earlier. The federal response to COVID-19 that he led was sclerotic. A newer generation of doctors and scientists, who had difficulty advancing during Fauci's tenure, might have been more open and flexible.

For all the good things he has done, Fauci, like sports greats Willie Mays and Muhammad Ali, hung on too long.

We need to boost COVID-19 surveillance to detect new viral variants

Cory Franklin Robert A. Weinstein *Chicago Tribune* 2·2·23

In the 1967 film *The Graduate*, the title character played by Dustin Hoffman attends a post-graduation party where a partygoer beckons him from the boisterous crowd and gives him a single word of career advice that has become an iconic cinema quote: "Plastics."

As COVID-19 retreats in the midwinter, the one word of advice for our scientific community going forward is "surveillance." The pandemic has forced us to relearn that public health surveillance — maintaining a watchful eye on new COVID-19 variants as well as other bacteria and viruses that threaten us — is the basis for preventing disease outbreaks and controlling them once they occur.

In many ways, public health surveillance is similar to a national government's intelligence surveillance. Both require a combination of human intelligence and technical sophistication to achieve their purpose. Espionage requires trained agents and high-tech equipment; public health demands expert healthcare personnel and advanced molecular diagnostic methods. Most important, in both cases, keeping citizens safe takes a global effort.

Right now, the greatest threat of a COVID-19 resurgence is from new coronavirus variants. The most important reservoir for those variants is China, where hundreds of millions of COVID-19 cases have been reported. Any one of China's many new cases could spawn a new variant, possibly more contagious and/or more virulent than what we have seen to date.

It is imperative that we work with China and other COVID-19 hot spots using the most advanced molecular techniques for identifying new viral variants. This means tracking data on COVID-19 cases and establishing and recording molecular profiles of circulating viruses to anticipate trends and tailor vaccine development. It will probably necessitate a collaborative worldwide network in conjunction with the World Health Organization. Unfortunately, to this point, China hasn't cooperated.

At home, we must ramp up one of the most important techniques developed during the pandemic — the deployment of wastewater sampling. The creation of an expanded national wastewater surveillance system by the Centers for Disease Control and Prevention to track the spread of COVID-19 variants is an early indicator of the rise or fall in COVID-19 cases and of new variants in a particular region. Wastewater sampling does not depend on whether people have COVID-19 symptoms or get tested.

Monitoring wastewater has added advantages including the possibility of discovering other viruses such as polio that threaten to reemerge in America. Wastewater sampling can assess the comparative success of COVID-19 control strategies in different regions of the country. To complement wastewater surveillance, it may soon be possible to employ airborne surveillance to look for COVID-19 and other aerosol or droplet-borne viruses aloft. Imagine not having to worry whether the crowded restaurant you enter has COVID-19 circulating above your table.

One of the difficulties during this phase of the pandemic has been ascertaining the true number of COVID-19 cases. In the U.S., there have been more than 100 million cases diagnosed and recorded by testing, but there are likely two to three times as many actual cases — people who have never been tested or those who tested at home and never reported the results. (Because the population of the U.S. is slightly more than 330 million, there can't be much more than three times as many cases, and this discounts those who have been reinfected.)

We don't know how much this undercount keeps us from measuring COVID-19 trends precisely. At-home testing has been a major advance in controlling spread and determining when to institute treatment. A system to report positive home tests automatically by mobile phone would be of immense benefit, and at-home tests are being developed for other potentially epidemic and treatable viruses such as influenza.

In the past, Google has attempted to predict seasonal flu patterns based on internet searches of symptoms and purchases of over-the-counter medicines. Results are mixed, but this, too, is a promising area for information technology to partner with public health to obtain real-time information. The CDC reporting system, by contrast, proved cumbersome early in the pandemic.

Twenty-eight years after his role in *The Graduate* made him a star, Hoffman starred in *Outbreak*, a riveting film about a deadly virus that threatens the U.S. Hoffman plays an Army doctor who specializes in disease control. He and his team must stop the spread of the virus before it infects the entire country, and his superior played by Morgan Freeman tells the team, "The fate of the nation, perhaps the world, is in our hands. We cannot, we dare not refuse this burden. I am confident each of you will do his duty." Life imitates art.

Suppressing debate on COVID-19 policies leads to mistrust in public health

Cory Franklin *Chicago Tribune* 2·7·23

China has abandoned its zero-COVID-19 campaign, and with the loosening of social restrictions, the country has shifted its focus from preventing COVID-19 infections to managing them. As part of that program, Li Guangxi, with China's State Council Joint Prevention and Control Mechanism, gave an interview last month encouraging people to take Chinese medicine for severe COVID-19, specifically ginger and Chinese ginseng, "the best ginseng in the world."

Are ginger and Chinese ginseng effective in fighting COVID-19? Who knows? There must be some studies out there somewhere. But that brief interview touting unproven medicines was startling. Think about what may have happened if an American scientist or official had given the same advice publicly. Hearing those recommendations, our medical influencers might have gone nuclear. A high public official in totalitarian China basically said things that conceivably could get a U.S. speaker censored or canceled by the American scientific establishment.

That's not such a stretch considering the case of Dr. Jay Bhattacharya. Bhattacharya, a tenured Stanford

University professor, was one of the authors of the Great Barrington Declaration, a proposal to protect high-risk populations rather than impose strict lockdowns during COVID-19. One of its points was keeping schools open during the pandemic.

Thanks to Twitter CEO Elon Musk's release of internal communications from the previous regime overseeing the social media platform, we learned that Twitter secretly censored and shadow-banned Bhattacharya. (Shadow-banning is an internal mechanism that makes it hard to read what someone posts on Twitter.)

Upon learning of what Twitter had done, Bhattacharya tweeted, "The thought that will keep me up tonight: censorship of scientific discussion permitted policies like school closures & a generation of children were hurt."

Like the efficacy of ginger and Chinese ginseng, the Great Barrington Declaration approach can be called into question — some parts may have been right; others may have been wrong. But the fallout from the dissent was clear. While he did not lose his tenure at Stanford, Bhattacharya was vilified and shunned by colleagues and many in the Stanford community. He received virtually no support from the Stanford administration.

It is discouraging to witness the extreme tactics the medical community has used to keep its members in line during the pandemic. Public intimidation, harassment, personal attacks, retraction of scientific papers after publication and career sabotage have been carried out with an eye toward bringing any dissenters in line, making sure they self-censor and refrain from expressing their views on controversial subjects such as the origin of COVID-19. Reader beware: It's as much what you don't read as what you do.

The medical community can enforce dogma internally, but rigorous censorship of dissenting scientific views can be effective only with the assistance of other powerful actors. As the Twitter experience demonstrated, the role of tech companies, especially Facebook and Google, cannot be discounted. Their reliance on internal fact-checkers and confidential editorial policies are often used as a means of controlling public discourse, and they have shown they favor a particular political vantage point.

Big Pharma has interests worth billions of dollars in the COVID-19 discussion, including vaccine development, emergency use authorization of drugs and future drug development. Questions that might adversely affect the financial interests of the pharmaceutical industry concerning any of these subjects are not especially welcome — but are necessary.

The real force multiplier for censorship of science is the government. The government must align closely with respected scientists and protect the public, but there is a fine line between that and reinforcing rigid scientific orthodoxy. By withholding National Institutes of Health grants, which some universities require a candidate to have before receiving tenure, the government can chill scientific opinions from academia it doesn't like.

Critics will point out that scientists must be vigilant against frauds and hucksters. True enough — there will always be charlatans and flimflammery ready to exploit the public. There will also be crackpots who deliberately disseminate false information along with the well-intentioned who unknowingly spout untruths. The best remedy is not to shut those opinions down, but to explain to the public clearly and consistently why they are wrong. COVID-19 is a lesson in how censoring opinion and suppressing debate stifles the approach to difficult scientific issues and creates mistrust in scientists and public health officials. In any scientific issue, impartial and open discussion is eminently preferable to "trust the consensus." To make informed decisions, the public must have access to many voices.

What is a reasonable approach to masking right now?

Cory Franklin Robert A. Weinstein *Chicago Tribune*
2·28·23

In medicine as elsewhere in life, if you ask the wrong question, you're likely to get the wrong answer. So if the question is, "Do masks worn outside medical settings work to protect against COVID-19 and respiratory diseases?" — or its politically charged companion, "Do you believe in masks?" — don't be surprised if the answers you receive are simplistic or wrong.

A perfect example was the recent publication of an analysis by the respected Cochrane Library, an organization that collates and reports the results of scientific studies. It examined a series of randomized controlled trials published in the scientific literature that asked whether surgical masks, N95 masks or P2 respirators prevented the transmission of respiratory viruses. The overarching consensus was that wearing a mask in ordinary public places "probably makes little or no difference" in an individual's risk of acquiring influenza or COVID-19.

The response by the news media and scientific community was predictable. Masking skeptics pounced, interpreting this to mean that masks are worthless, thus ignoring the words "probably" and "little or no difference" that leave open the possibility of benefit at the margins or in high-risk settings, which can exert a dramatic effect in a large population. Meanwhile, masking defenders mounted a vigorous takedown of the report and an impassioned defense of masks as essential.

There are limitations to the Cochrane report, but it cannot be dismissed. It suggests that studies promoted by the Centers for Disease Control and Prevention and World Health Organization early in the pandemic that cited high degrees of mask effectiveness were overstated. According to one study, the chances of acquiring COVID-19 were reduced by nearly 80% by wearing a mask. An effect this significant should have shown up — but didn't — in the Cochrane compendium.

This is not proof that masks are not effective, but it does strengthen the argument that the effect of masks is limited. (The young person you may have seen biking alone along the lake wearing a mask but no helmet doesn't understand the concept of relative risk.) That's why the question asked in the studies is so important. If the question asked is not whether masks work but whether they have a role in selected situations, the Cochrane report comes up short. The report concentrated on randomized controlled trials, in which subjects are divided by chance (to eliminate selection bias) into separate groups to study whether a drug or an intervention like masking really works. The randomized controlled trial, or RCT, is touted as the gold standard of experimental design, but one of the things we have learned from the pandemic is that this is not always true.

"Over the last 30 years or so, I have begun to realize that while RCTs are a brilliant idea for testing drugs, they are a catastrophically bad idea for testing certain other things, masks being one of them. There are a lot of philosophical reasons, but there are also common-sense reasons," Dr. Trisha Greenhalgh, a respected British professor at the University of Oxford who studies mask effect, explained in a 2022 Medscape interview.

"The RCT is an artificial thing. You randomize people to A or B, and you have to keep everything controlled. The thing about masking in a community in the real world is you cannot control everything. In fact, you can control very little. If I ask you to give your consent to wear a mask and then get tested for COVID-19, that's great because you have given informed consent. But what about everybody else in the community?" Greenhalgh asked.

Given these limitations, what is a reasonable approach to masking right now? As the director of the CDC, Dr. Rochelle Walensky has stated much depends on community levels of COVID-19. When levels are high, there are more situations, such as long stints in crowded indoor venues with poor ventilation, in which masking is prudent. When levels are moderate to low, as they are now, masks are irrelevant in most settings.

The greatest benefit to masking remains in healthcare settings in areas with immunocompromised patients — for example, organ transplant areas and chemotherapy wards. There is historical evidence that masks, especially N95 masks, have prevented infections in these areas. When community levels are low, policies for routine masking in other hospital areas are best left to individual institutions. (Virus transmission may still occur outside patient rooms.)

In schools, we believe masks should be optional for teachers and students, especially at current community levels. COVID-19 transmission by children is low, but not zero, and many countries no longer require masking in school. We believe masking does harm language and social development in younger students — another situation in which studies have not answered the questioned conclusively. Masking may be recommended for students and teachers who are immunocompromised.

In his 1982 classic book *Medical Thinking*, the eminent medical historian Dr. Lester King described scientific evolution in medicine over centuries. He asked a fundamental question, "Do we recognize the enormous gulf between 'This is true' and 'This is true only under limited circumstances'?" That question is central to understanding the complex role of masks in respiratory disease.

Excess deaths in the US are rising at a shocking rate

Cory Franklin Robert A. Weinstein *Chicago Tribune* 4·10·23

The current COVID-19 situation in the U.S. is both good and bad. The good news is that COVID-19 deaths are at the lowest levels of the three-year pandemic. Given current trends, projections indicate roughly 100,000 COVID-19 deaths for 2023 — less than half of any of the three previous years. The bad news is that the number of overall excess U.S. deaths — the difference between expected numbers of deaths from all causes and the actual number of deaths observed — is rising at a shocking rate. COVID-19 is a factor, but the main causes of excess deaths are more social than medical, and the worst aspect is that they are occurring in the younger demographic in which homicides, suicides, vehicular deaths and drugs are taking a disproportionate toll on what should be the healthiest sector of the population.

Since the pandemic began, excess deaths are up by more than 1.25 million in the U.S., about 15% higher than in the pre-pandemic years. This pattern is not limited to the U.S.; excess pandemic deaths are elevated by 5% to 20% in Great Britain, most of Europe and Australia. The reason for these excess deaths defies simple explanation;

the cause is certainly multifactorial. Some of this is likely an undercount of COVID-19 deaths. Another factor is delayed deaths caused by past COVID-19 infections. After any acute viral infection like COVID-19 has subsided, patients can suffer long-term medical complications including problems with inflammation and dangerous blood clotting disorders. These late effects of COVID-19 have included increases in fatal heart attacks and strokes.

In the arena of excess deaths, unanticipated effects of lockdowns that resulted in healthcare and societal disruptions have been just as important as COVID-19 itself. Patients have found it more difficult to access care. Appointments with physicians have been delayed; routine surgeries, including biopsies, have been canceled; and even when patients suffer symptoms, many have avoided clinics and hospitals, fearing COVID-19 or just long waits. While telemedicine has helped many people, suspicious lumps cannot be diagnosed on Zoom. In the U.S., diagnosis rates of six common cancers fell between 16% and 42% during the early days of the pandemic. These figures probably understate the number of serious conditions that were discovered late or not at all.

Combine this with deaths of despair (suicides and overdoses), vehicular accidents (possibly faster and more reckless driving) and homicides. Further, add the deaths that were occasioned by the unhealthy lifestyle choices —

overeating and excessive drinking — prompted by lockdowns. While the fairly strict lockdowns of the U.S., Australia and Western Europe have clearly contributed to excess deaths, Sweden is notable because government pandemic restrictions were not nearly as stringent and there were fewer lockdown deaths. Initially, Sweden was criticized for its more lenient approach to the pandemic, but Sweden has had one of the lowest total excess mortality rates in Europe since the beginning of the pandemic.

There is also a minority theory that vaccine complications have contributed to excess deaths. However, there is no reliable data from any country supporting this belief, and the experience of Sweden, which has a higher full vaccination rate than the world average, belies this notion.

The most depressing aspect of this excess death phenomenon is that life expectancy in the U.S. has dropped for the second consecutive year. Current life expectancy in the U.S. is 76.4 years, the lowest figure of the past two decades. After World War II, American longevity was the envy of the world. Now we have fallen behind Lebanon, Cuba and Czechia. All this is in the face of improved care for the elderly: The U.S. has comparable survival after age 75 with industrialized countries, better control of cardiovascular risk factors, lower stroke mortality, and higher rates of cancer screening and survival.

The alarming truth is that the decrease in U.S. life expectancy has come at the expense of teenagers, young adults and those in early middle age. This is not the result of COVID-19; in 2021 alone, more potential years of American life were lost because of drugs (primarily opiates), road deaths, firearm violence and obesity than years lost from COVID-19 during the entire pandemic.

In *The Tempest,* William Shakespeare cautioned that "what's past is prologue." Englishman John Burn-Murdoch, a columnist for the *Financial Times,* has studied mortality patterns in the U.S. and United Kingdom and warns, "One in 25 American five-year-olds today will not make it to their 40th birthday. No parent should ever have to bury their child, but on average across the US one set of parents from every kindergarten class most likely will."

Surely a clarion call, to which America must respond immediately.

Did COVID-19 cause pediatric hepatitis? Skepticism helped find an answer

Cory Franklin Robert A. Weinstein *Chicago Tribune*
4·20·23

Two qualities a first-class science journalist and a first-class physician must have are patience and a skeptical nature. If a new disease appears somewhere, the journalist and the physician need the skepticism to reject easy explanations of the source. As it has been said of war, first impressions are often wrong. The public may lose interest in the disease if it disappears, but the professionals, knowing the disease may reappear, must be patient in uncovering its origins, even if it takes years.

This happened in spring 2022 when nearly 350 otherwise healthy children in the U.S. suddenly contracted an unusually severe form of hepatitis. At least another 1,000 worldwide came down with the disease. According to the World Health Organization, 22 children died, and another 46 required liver transplants.

The usual precipitating causes of hepatitis, generally a benign illness in children, were quickly eliminated. The source became a medical mystery, and coming in the wake of the omicron wave of COVID-19, some observers concluded that either COVID-19 or the vaccine had caused hepatitis. Simply from a temporal standpoint, a causal association seemed logical, even though the Centers for Disease Control and Prevention and public health authorities in Israel and Great Britain were skeptical, especially of a link to vaccines. At the time, no cause was conclusively established, and most of the cases subsided as quickly as they had appeared.

The mysterious cases of severe pediatric hepatitis fell off the public radar, so it was left for physicians in the U.S. and United Kingdom to pursue the matter. A year later, researchers have published three studies in the journal *Nature* that may provide the answer. The most important finding was that there appears to be no link between the acute liver disease in children and COVID-19 infection vaccines.

All three studies found that only a small minority of patients had COVID-19 infections. (In two of the studies, none of the affected children had COVID-19.) Regarding a possible vaccine cause, most children had not been vaccinated, and in fact, the outbreak in the U.K. occurred before most children were eligible for the vaccine. With so few children receiving the vaccine, it was essentially ruled out as a cause for the acute liver disease.

So what had happened? The studies demonstrated that the likely cause of hepatitis in children was an interaction of two typically benign non-COVID- 19-related viruses. (For the record, the two viruses are adenovirus and

AAV2.) Most of the affected children had a specific genetic susceptibility associated with autoimmune conditions. This suggests that in some way the two viruses acted synergistically and caused the body to react against the liver.

While COVID-19 did not cause pediatric hepatitis, it may have been indirectly involved as a result of public health efforts to contain the virus. The U.K. researchers postulated that the measures to reduce the spread of COVID-19 may have led to less public exposure to viruses in general and resulted in reduced immunity. As lockdowns loosened and schools reopened, the two responsible viruses began circulating among children. Many children became infected for the first time and subsequently infected others. Some of those who were genetically susceptible developed hepatitis.

There are several offshoots to the pediatric hepatitis story. Before COVID-19, we had a limited knowledge of how many cases of pediatric hepatitis there were on a national basis. Once cases began appearing in children, the U.S. and other countries started surveilling the condition, so we developed a better understanding of how many cases of hepatitis typically occur in children. When an abnormally high number appears, it gave us an early warning of a potential outbreak. Moreover, severe acute hepatitis is traditionally uncommon in children, and in nearly half the cases, the cause is unknown. Now that we are aware of the interaction of these two viruses causing hepatitis, it opens up new avenues for diagnosis and treatment.

The American journalist H.L. Mencken once said, "Every complex problem has a solution which is simple, direct, plausible — and wrong." It was tempting to believe that COVID-19 was responsible for the 2022 worldwide wave of severe pediatric hepatitis; it turned out not to be true.

That's why good science journalists and physicians should be skeptical and patient. Because in science, things are not always as they seem at first.

Why does a rich country like the US have a high COVID-19 death rate?

Cory Franklin *Chicago Tribune* 5·11·23

Following his recent retirement, Dr. Anthony Fauci reflected on his government role during the COVID-19 pandemic. When asked about the high per capita COVID-19 death rate in the U.S., Fauci replied, "Something clearly went wrong. And I don't know exactly what it was. But the reason we know it went wrong is that we are the richest country in the world, and on a per capita basis we've done worse than virtually all other countries. And there's no reason that a rich country like ours has to have 1.1 million deaths. Unacceptable."

What did he mean by that? His implication seems to be that there should be a correlation between a nation's wealth and a lower per capita COVID-19 death rate. If so, it follows that our rich country should have a low per capita death rate; since we don't, we must be doing something fundamentally wrong.

That's a logical assumption and a common sentiment in the news media and among many experts. Studies linking COVID-19 deaths to poverty in the U.S. do not answer the question because they have sometimes failed to account for confounding variables — Are residents in poorer states older, fatter, with more diabetes? — or they have used data from the first half of the pandemic (death patterns have shifted somewhat since the appearance of the omicron variant).

There is one overall problem with the theory that wealthy countries have lower per capita COVID-19 death rates: It is contradicted by actual worldwide outcomes. There is no evidence that national wealth protects against COVID-19 deaths. It is a complex scenario, but in fact, the evidence suggests the opposite — when all countries are considered, COVID-19 may be primarily a disease of affluent countries.

When he drew a correlation between a country's wealth and a low per capita death rate, Fauci, who has been quoted as saying, "I represent science," appears to have ignored the worldwide data — a distinctly unscientific approach. Much of the scientific community and news media focus on COVID-19 outcomes from Western Europe, Canada, Japan and Australia to draw conclusions. Those conclusions are not supported by outcomes that include the world's poorest countries.

Staring at us are the figures from Africa: Per-capita COVID-19 deaths on that continent are one-sixteenth that of the U.S. and, in some of the poorer countries, much lower than that. Africa, the poorest continent, with 17% of the world's population, has registered less than 4% of the world's COVID-19 deaths. It doesn't take a statistician, a

PhD or an army of graduate students to realize there can't be much of a correlation between national wealth and COVID-19 mortality.

The immediate rejoinder is that there has been bad data collection and poor reporting of COVID-19 deaths in Africa. This does not begin to explain why in places such as Nigeria and Benin, if only 1% of the deaths were being reported — which itself would be pretty much impossible to conceal from the public — the per capita death totals would still be less than half the per capita death rate of the U.S.

The reason Africa is faring better is not poor reporting, dollars spent, public health measures/infrastructure, medical treatments or even vaccination. (Africa is the only continent where less than 50% of the population is vaccinated against COVID-19.) It is probably because Africa has more open environments, a younger population not as susceptible to the virus, a lower rate of obesity especially in sub-Saharan Africa and less diabetes. Factors such as genetic resistance in the African population and protective immunity from past exposure, which might affect outcomes, are also subjects for future investigation.

The situation is, of course, reversed in most of the industrialized world — an older, more obese world. There are variations on that theme — why certain countries have a lower per capita death rate than others — that may have to do in small part with how the pandemic was managed, but the differences are much more likely to be due to the medical profile of each population and the associated population immunity to COVID-19, either natural or acquired.

While the world's richest countries have per capita death rates below that of the U.S., none of them is distinguished by having especially low rates internationally. Put simply, none of the wealthiest countries had a magic bullet that made its COVID-19 death rates "acceptable," to use Fauci's term.

The virus is, and always has been, the pandemic's main actor. Our actions can save lives — yes, and that is important — but when you are talking about millions of COVID-19 deaths, what we do has affected this only at the margins. The data from Africa, and some other poor countries, strongly suggests Fauci's hubris, and that of others, was to ascribe an agency to our actions we never possessed.

We are in the back seat blithely giving directions, while the virus is firmly ensconced in the driver's seat, controlling the car. And it doesn't matter whether the car is a late-model Tesla or an old beat-up Ford.

Ventilators and the learning curve of COVID-19 treatment

Cory Franklin Robert A. Weinstein *Chicago Tribune*
5·23·23

An axiom in medicine is that good judgment depends on experience, and experience depends on bad judgment. Basically, one way doctors refine their care is through a learning curve resulting from inexperience and lack of judgment. A fitting example during the COVID-19 pandemic was the worldwide experience with ventilators, which are used to support lung function in patients with serious COVID-19 pneumonia.

Viruses or bacteria that invade the lungs and cause pneumonia impair the body's ability to take in oxygen. When this becomes severe, it is known as hypoxemia (this is what those finger oximeters measure.) In advanced hypoxemia, patients experience shortness of breath. If it worsens, they will be unable to breathe. At that point, doctors will insert a tube in the windpipe and attach the tube to a ventilator, which takes over a patient's breathing until the lungs heal.

In March 2020, with COVID-19 ravaging Italy, Western Europe and New York City, deaths from COVID-19 pneumonia began increasing exponentially. Body bags were stacking up in New York hospital morgues, and health officials nationally became concerned about an anticipated shortage of ventilators, which became a political issue with mayors and governors jousting to acquire more ventilators.

"This is a story about doing the impossible," then New York Mayor Bill de Blasio boasted at the height of the crisis. "We'd never made a ventilator before — and so we made thousands. We learned it would take a year — and so we did it in a month." General Motors and Ford also started a World War II-type manufacturing campaign to deliver new supplies of the devices suddenly deemed critical to the COVID-19 effort.

One problem: No one had any idea how many ventilators would be necessary. Estimates were all over the map. "There is a broad range of estimates of the number of ventilators we will need to care for U.S. patients with COVID-19, from several hundred thousand to as many as a million," several physicians and public health experts wrote in the *New England Journal of Medicine* in April 2020. "The national strategic reserve of ventilators is small and far from sufficient for the projected gap. No matter which estimate we use, there are not enough ventilators for patients with COVID-19 in the upcoming months."

For a short time, there were temporary ventilator shortages in certain regions, but the estimates from the *New England Journal of Medicine* turned out to be too high. The situation soon changed dramatically with two unexpected developments.

First, doctors noticed that COVID-19 patients did not always improve as anticipated when placed on ventilators. Both in the U.S. and Europe, these patients were actually dying at a higher rate than expected. Ventilators may have been applied too quickly, and it is now believed they actually caused some of those deaths, either as a result of the aggravating damage done by forcing air into the lungs or from other microorganisms entering the lungs more easily down breathing tubes. Ventilators undoubtedly saved many patients, and many of those who died would have died anyway, but it is likely that of the nearly 2.5 million worldwide COVID-19 deaths in the first year of the pandemic, several thousand were directly the result of ventilator complications.

The second development was that, for poorly understood reasons, some patients with COVID-19 pneumonia and severe hypoxemia did not experience shortness of breath in the same manner as patients with other diseases. Doctors were astonished to see patients with otherwise life-threatening low oxygen levels walking around their hospital rooms or talking on their cellphones. This gave physicians latitude to use alternative treatments to inserting breathing tubes and ventilators. Some medical centers in Europe and North America (UChicago Medicine was one of the first) successfully began using high-flow nasal cannula systems, turning patients on their stomachs, and employing masks similar to those used in sleep apnea, often successfully raising oxygen levels to safe values.

While ventilators are still essential for some COVID-19 patients, the pattern of use has changed dramatically. In the early days of the pandemic, data from the Centers for Disease Control and Prevention shows that 25% of all hospitalized COVID-19 patients were placed on ventilators. Today that figure is 5%. There are many causes for the decrease: vaccination, a less severe virus and (with the early pandemic deaths of the most susceptible) fewer vulnerable patients. But there is no question that a learning curve and change in practice was part of that equation.

Recently in New York City nearly 3,000 ventilators, which originally cost taxpayers $12 million, were sold for less than $25,000. A Long Island junk dealer used 28 trucks to haul off many of the ventilators Mayor de Blasio touted three years ago.

In medicine, what seems true today might not be true tomorrow, and no one knows whether it will be true the day after tomorrow. In retrospect, the 2020 controversy over having enough ventilators proved mostly unwarranted and resulted in unnecessary expense. But we couldn't know that at the time — we had to err on the side of having too many rather than too few ventilators. Still, the virus threw us surprise curveballs that resulted in dramatic changes in the treatment for hypoxemia in severe COVID-19 pneumonia. Planning for future pandemics is not as easy as it is sometimes portrayed. The takeaway for future pandemic strategists is to factor in a good degree of flexibility — because nature never runs short on curveballs.

If a lab leak led to COVID-19, there are truths we must not ignore

Cory Franklin Robert A. Weinstein *Chicago Tribune*
6·26·23

Since 2019 when COVID-19 emerged in China, scientists worldwide have been trying to ascertain the origin of the virus. The two major theories are a natural spillover from bats to an animal source and then to humans or a laboratory accident. A related question is whether the virus emerged from nature or was the result of human-made genetic manipulation.

Until recently, although no animal intermediary between virus-carrying bats and humans has been identified, Chinese scientists and many of their Western counterparts, including prominent American researchers, argued that animals transmitted the virus to humans. They downplayed the lab leak theory and essentially dismissed the possibility that the virus was engineered rather than a creation of nature.

Particularly notable was a report on the pandemic's origin released in March 2021 by the World Health Organization, which failed to identify the source of the virus but claimed an animal source was "likely to very likely." Only a few pages of the report and its annexes addressed the possibility of a laboratory accident, and a lab leak was deemed so unlikely that the virus having been carried into China on frozen food packages was posed as a more probable explanation.

This scenario strained credulity but was a convenient way of shifting the blame away from China, which had a say in determining which facts outsiders could investigate. Not incidentally, the natural-origin theory also protected Chinese scientists and their foreign sources of funding from inconvenient questions about safety protocols and the wisdom or foolishness of dangerous research projects.

In the past year as the pandemic wound down, the "very likely" theory of an animal vector has been met with increasing skepticism. Many in the scientific community, as well as some in U.S. intelligence circles, do not buy the remarkable coincidence that the first COVID-19 cases just happened to appear in Wuhan, China, the site of the Chinese government-run Wuhan Institute of Virology. FBI Director Christopher Wray has said that the bureau believes COVID-19 most likely originated in a Chinese government-controlled lab.

Now out is a comprehensive investigation of the virus origin by the *Sunday Times* of London, compiled with extensive sourcing including interviews with U.S. State Department special investigators who have been studying the origin of COVID-19 and have amassed secret intelligence on events in China before COVID-19 emerged.

The conclusion of *Times* reporters was startling. "Scientists in Wuhan working alongside the Chinese military were combining the world's most deadly coronaviruses to create a new mutant virus just as the pandemic began. Investigators who scrutinized top-secret intercepted communications and scientific research believe Chinese scientists were running a covert project of dangerous experiments, which caused a leak from the Wuhan Institute of Virology and started the COVID-19 outbreak. The U.S. investigators say one of the reasons there is no published information on the work is because it was done in collaboration with researchers from the Chinese military, which was funding it and which, they say, was pursuing bioweapons."

While the *Times* does not claim the virus was intended to be a bioweapon, the findings bolster the lab leak theory and support it by noting the first cases of COVID-19 likely occurred in Chinese researchers involved in the early lab work at Wuhan. Journalists from other news outlets also have reported that the virology institute scientists were the first humans to be infected.

Moreover, scientists from the Chinese military working at the Wuhan institute were coincidentally involved in vaccine development just before the international outbreak. The *Times* also fleshes out unsettling details previously reported. The U.S. government gave more than $1 million in research funding to the virology institute through an intermediary organization, and an American virus expert provided critical research to the Chinese by exploring the potential for a vaccine while being well aware of the dangers of his research.

Now that the pandemic is over, what difference does it make how it started? This is a significant moment. If the *Times* investigation is substantially true, there are at least three disturbing conclusions:

First, if the Chinese cannot be trusted to provide reliable information and their military is actively working on bioweapons, that's ominous. We are still involved in global rivalries that hark back to the Cold War, and an emerging battlefield is the scientific laboratory. The potential exists for the proliferation of weapons as deadly as nuclear ones — but harder to detect. Washington shouldn't be providing research funds for China or any other country if U.S. officials cannot tell how the money is being used.

Second, this episode dispels the notion that scientists are an apolitical community that can work without regard to international borders — a lesson we must continuously relearn in the face of the profession's protestations to the contrary. During World War II, many of the nuclear physicists who worked on the Manhattan Project were committed pacifists and internationalists. But they subordinated their beliefs, knowing what the Nazis would do if German physicists delivered the atomic bomb to Adolf Hitler first.

Third, just as a politicized United Nations cannot guarantee world peace, the politicized WHO cannot guarantee biosecurity — these organizations are necessary but not sufficient. The U.S. should explore NATO-type independent alliances to create a distant early warning system that includes real-time international genomic, case and wastewater surveillance for dangerous biological agents. Presidential candidates from both parties should describe their plans for forming such an alliance.

Hard truths, to be sure. But unless we acknowledge and respond to these truths, as bad as COVID-19 was, the inevitable next pandemic could be much worse.

The US bungled its COVID-19 vaccine distribution. Why no accountability?

Cory Franklin Robert A. Weinstein *Chicago Tribune*
8·14·23

Although the lion's share of COVID-19 infections and deaths in the United States is over, Americans should embrace their inner Yogi Berra, who once observed that "it ain't over till it's over."

Indeed, a number of issues regarding COVID-19 remain active, including hundreds of thousands of patients potentially stricken with long COVID-19 and the mystery of the virus's origin. But among the most important and least appreciated issues is a public accounting of how the vaccine was distributed and administered throughout the country. The vaccine distribution system was not our finest hour, and the process must be upgraded for future health emergencies.

Whatever one believes about Donald Trump, Operation Warp Speed was one of the most effective research projects ever undertaken. Considering the time pressures, employing an mRNA platform permitted rapid development of a vaccine that was relatively safe and resulted in fairly effective protection from hospitalization and death.

The success of Warp Speed was tempered almost immediately by distribution. The first test was meeting demand for the vaccine when there was a limited supply and no ability to direct demand to where the vaccine actually existed. This, coupled with the daunting task of shipping and storing the rapidly perishable vaccine (after the seal was punctured, every dose had to go into an arm; otherwise, the unused doses were discarded the same day), represented a significant logistical challenge.

Distribution went from federal to state and local governments then to healthcare providers and community groups. The result was a confusing patchwork of distribution policies from the government, national healthcare entities, state governments, local public health departments and the ultimate providers: hospitals, pharmacies, fire departments and jails. Even where there was an adequate supply of vaccine, it was often difficult to impossible to locate. Is it any wonder low-level chaos ensued? How many times was a provider or pharmacy asked, "Do you have the vaccine?"

Distribution policies were not simply confusing. For example, New York senior citizens faced a 51-step online registration process including multiple uploads of information. They also were often contradictory. By common agreement, essential workers received the vaccine first, but after that, politics played an outsize role. In certain locations, those with preexisting conditions and the elderly — who were most likely to die from COVID-19 — received lower priority in favor of low-risk patients in the name of "public health equity."

Powerful teachers unions secured a priority status for teachers in many jurisdictions, even for many educators whose schools had closed. And residency restrictions meant people might be turned away if they traveled to a neighboring county to get vaccinated, even if the distribution site was much closer than one in their home county. Remember: The goal was to get every available dose into a waiting patient's arm, but these shambolic approaches meant wasted vaccine and potentially lives lost.

In too many instances, providers and the government tracking systems did not know exactly where "their" vaccine was. There were few reliable websites or maps that the public could consult. A group of private volunteers in California set up a workable phone tree to identify the location of available vaccines, based on the most reliable sources they identified: local pharmacists and pharmacy chains.

According to data from the Centers for Disease Control and Prevention, pharmacies, states, U.S. territories and federal agencies discarded 82.1 million COVID-19 vaccine doses from December 2020 through mid-May

2022 — just over 11% of the doses the federal government distributed.

All too often, the goal seemed to be deciding who would get the one dose the system could administer capably, but little effort was put into guaranteeing the four remaining doses in the vial went to eagerly waiting patients. The decision at some vaccination sites to discard unused vaccine at the end of the day was scandalous. In Israel, providers simply went out into the street and gave the day's unused vaccine doses to anyone who wanted them.

Another scandal was the part played by our multitrillion-dollar tech industry — Google, Apple, Microsoft, Facebook and Amazon, the greatest knowledge-based system the world has ever known. These companies can ship and track any delivery, map the entire country precisely, store virtually everyone's personal information and create super-sophisticated websites. Yet they seemed to work at arm's length from the government. Where were their skills in the vaccine distribution scheme as people wasted time, low-tech style, frantically dialing their phones looking for vaccine doses? What was their exact obligation to the public to streamline distribution — contractual with the government or moral? Either way, some of the country's unused vaccine and COVID-19 mortality can be attributed to tech industry inertia.

And the biggest scandal of all? To date, there has been no comprehensive debrief on how the federal and many local governments bungled the country's COVID-19 vaccine distribution plan for 2021 to 2023 — no public post-mortem, no national commission, no published report and no accountability from whatever entity was ultimately in charge. As the pandemic, with its crowded emergency departments, packed intensive care units and morgues, fades from our collective memory, there is diminishing imperative to create a more effective mass vaccination plan for the next pandemic.

What reason do we have to believe the next time will be better? Besides our inner Yogi Berra, we might also want to channel our inner Benjamin Franklin who noted that "by failing to prepare, you are preparing to fail."

What should we expect from COVID-19 this fall?

Cory Franklin Robert A. Weinstein *Chicago Tribune* 10·3·23

The changing leaves of fall mark the country's fourth autumn with COVID-19. Although most reporting is anecdotal, new variants have caused case counts to rise. The number of new cases in the country was recently the highest since last winter but still far below case totals during the last three autumns.

The reporting of hospitalizations and deaths is more accurate than that of case counts, and the news is optimistic. While hospitalizations have risen significantly, paralleling cases, the numbers are proportionately fewer than in previous years. Deaths are rising but not significantly, and overall mortality from COVID-19 is dropping, slowly but steadily. This is probably the result of a combination of acquired population immunity (vaccination and previous infection) and reduced severity of the current variants.

A dramatic uptick in COVID-19 cases or an emerging, more lethal variant could leave the country in the lurch, especially in light of the questionable decision by public health entities to cut back on case reporting. In light of this lack of knowledge, what can the public do? The response should be to demand better reporting by physicians, public health officials and science journalists. Here are six topics we should know more about.

Current COVID-19 trends: Tracking COVID-19 cases and trends has become more difficult, in part because of home testing. Public health officials have largely abandoned anything other than wastewater virus surveillance. "We have essentially given up on other types of surveillance," said Bill Hanage, an associate director at the Center for Communicable Disease Dynamics at Harvard University. "People are testing at home. ... The only way we really have of keeping hold of what pandemic activity is going on is through stuff like wastewater. ... That's about as close as we can (get) to forecasting." We can still appreciate large shifts in COVID-19 trends by measuring wastewater, hospitalizations and deaths, but more sensitive surveillance methods are still necessary. There is a need for innovative ideas, perhaps a trial of QR codes on home test kits to allow "citizen surveillance" reporting and/or tracking pharmacy prescriptions for the COVID-19-specific medication Paxlovid.

Vaccines: As COVID-19 evolves with emerging variants, every new booster is unique. Boosters must be developed rapidly in preparation for new outbreaks; therefore, much of the data on effectiveness comes from testing immune responses in animals. It takes time to obtain real-world results in adults. The public needs up-to-date information on how the new generations of vaccines actually perform in patients, along with potential side effects incurred. The information should be readily accessible and easily understandable to lay readers.

Long COVID-19: Long COVID-19 — persistent, lingering symptoms from previous COVID-19 infection — is a potential problem for millions of Americans. Yet estimates of the number of patients affected vary significantly because there are no agreed-on definitions of what constitutes long COVID-19. Moreover, adequate control groups are important because many symptoms seen in people with past COVID-19 infection are also seen in patients who have not had COVID-19. How big a problem do we face, and how do we know?

COVID-19 and obesity: Obesity is a major risk factor, possibly the major risk factor, for death from COVID-19. The U.S. obesity epidemic is one explanation as to why the U.S. has more than one million COVID-19 deaths, far more than any other country. New research and recent treatments have brought a revolution in the care of obesity. This raises the questions of whether vaccines and treatment work as well in obese patients and whether healthy eating campaigns and the obesity medications recently approved by the Food and Drug Administration could be targeted at patients at especially high risk for COVID-19.

COVID-19 social isolation: This year, the U.S. surgeon general released an advisory about the public health crisis of loneliness and social isolation in the country. This was aggravated by lockdowns during the COVID-19 epidemic, and this continues to be a problem that has likely aggravated the distressing suicide rate in the country. Last year, nearly 50,000 people died by suicide, according to the Centers for Disease Control and Prevention. We should direct more effort to combating personal isolation and maintaining family and social connections.

COVID-19 genetics: Genetics plays an important role in COVID-19 infections, and it has become clear that certain genes are associated with stronger clinical and immunologic responses to COVID-19. This is one explanation for why some COVID-19 patients get life-threatening infections while others get the sniffles. It has been recognized since early in the pandemic that when domestic partners are infected simultaneously, one may get much sicker than the other (and it is not unusual for one partner to stay uninfected while the other gets sick). Certain areas of the world, such as Singapore and central Africa, have exceedingly low COVID-19 mortality rates that may be related to genetics. This aspect of COVID-19 should be a much bigger story than it is currently and has implications in the future for COVID-19 and personalized medicine.

Rising numbers of cases and hospitalizations have peaked for now, but there is still consternation about COVID-19 misinformation. Yet the larger threat to the public is the lack of information in so many spheres. Ben Hogan, one of the 20th century's greatest golfers, once said, "The average golfer's problem is not so much the lack of ability as it is lack of knowledge about what he should be doing."

In that respect, COVID-19 is a lot like golf.

What is the mortality of COVID-19?

Cory Franklin *Chicago Tribune* 10·13·23

Since the pandemic began, there have been wide-ranging estimates about COVID-19 mortality — what percentage of those who have contracted the virus have not survived. Until recently, public health researchers have not had sufficient information to address the question with precision. After nearly four years, though, we have truly useful data.

So, what is the mortality of COVID-19?

It takes not one figure, but three, to answer that question. All three mortality figures involve assumptions, and the numbers change over time, but patterns are emerging. All three figures employ the total number of U.S. COVID-19 deaths as the numerator. (Caution: There will be math, but only long division. The numerator is the top number.)

Since January 2020, according to data compiled by Worldometer, there have been roughly 1.1 million to 1.2 million U.S. COVID-19 deaths. Some experts doubt that figure, claiming deaths from COVID-19 should be distinguished from deaths with COVID-19 (such as the person who dies in a motorcycle accident who tests positive at the hospital.) It's a fair criticism, and a reasonable estimate is that deaths with COVID-19 account for 10% of the total figure.

However, it is likely that perhaps 10% of people who died from COVID-19 were never tested — those who died at home or died suddenly. A workable assumption is that those who died with COVID-19 and those who were never tested but died of COVID-19 cancel out. The number of COVID-19 deaths, 1.1 million to 1.2 million Americans over the course of the pandemic, is a reasonable estimate.

The other half of the mortality equation is the denominator or bottom number: the number of COVID-19 cases. Because case numbers change over time, COVID-19 mortality cannot be described by a single figure. Each of the three figures describes how dangerous COVID-19 is and the likelihood of death in an individual person who contracts COVID-19.

The first mortality figure is the case fatality rate, the ratio of COVID-19 deaths divided by reported cases of COVID-19. There have been approximately 108.5 million reported U.S. COVID-19 cases. This number increases as more people are diagnosed.

The cumulative case fatality rate of COVID-19 in the U.S. (deaths divided by reported cases) since the pandemic began in January 2020 is 1.05% to 1.10% (1.1 million to 1.2 million divided by 108.5 million).

Basically, from January 2020 until today, if you had a reported case of COVID-19 in the U.S., your chances of dying were a little more than 1 in 100.

The number of actual cases is obviously greater than the number of reported cases, and 108.5 million is a significant undercount, since many COVID-19 cases are never reported due to home testing or lack of testing. The true number can't be measured definitively, but based on several variables, we can make a decent estimate. The current assumption is that 90% of the U.S. populace of 334 million has had at least one COVID-19 infection. For convenience of computation, about 300 million is the case estimate.

The second mortality number is the infection fatality rate, the ratio of deaths divided by the number of estimated actual cases.

The infection fatality rate of COVID-19 in the U.S. (deaths divided by total estimated cases) since January 2020 is 0.36% to 0.40% (1.1 million to 1.2 million divided by 300 million).

That is, if you had a COVID-19 infection, reported or not, your chances of dying were 3 to 4 in 1,000. Home-tested and unreported cases were less likely to die, explaining the lower figure than the case fatality rate.

The third mortality number is called crude mortality, the number of confirmed deaths divided by the entire population of the US. It includes everyone, including those who have not had COVID-19.

The current crude mortality of COVID-19 in the U.S. (deaths divided by total population) is 0.33% to 0.36% (1.1 million to 1.2 million divided by 334 million).

Bottom line: The chance any person in the U.S. would die of COVID-19 since the beginning of the pandemic is roughly 1 in 300. This is the best number to compare between countries. The crude mortality worldwide is roughly 0.09%, one-quarter that of the U.S. — the U.S. is a high-risk country because of our population's advanced age and existing health conditions such as obesity.

However, there are three caveats to this data.

First, the case fatality and infection fatality rates — the chances an individual with COVID-19 will die — have been dropping dramatically since the pandemic began. The rates were much higher in 2020 than today and have been falling continuously, likely due to acquired population immunity, vaccination, the sickest having died and the arrival of possibly less severe variants.

The current U.S. infection fatality rate, 0.4% on the high end since the pandemic began, is probably now about

0.1% for new cases, one-third to one-quarter the cumulative number. A random patient with COVID-19 today has a 1-in-1,000 chance of dying, roughly the same as having moderately severe flu.

Second, these average figures do not account for individual risk or vaccination status. The figure for a low-risk patient today may be one-tenth to one-one-hundredth as low: 0.01% to 0.001% — a chance of dying of 1 in 10,000 to 1 in 100,000 — in the neighborhood of having mild flu.

Finally, these figures pertain only to mortality, not to long COVID-19, an important question in which the relative risks are still being studied.

The current figures put COVID-19 mortality into perspective against influenza. In terms of mortality, at its height in 2020-21, COVID-19 was far more severe than most influenza strains, especially in high-risk COVID-19 patients, although never as severe as the 1918-19 flu pandemic.

Today, for high-risk patients, COVID-19 is still more severe than most strains of influenza, but for low-risk patients, COVID-19 mortality has approached that of the average annual flu.

The incalculable damage wrought by COVID-19 is everywhere

Cory Franklin *Chicago Tribune* 1·8·24

The ledger on COVID-19 has been closed for 2023. But the contagion is not, as some have proclaimed, "over" with the Upper Midwest dealing with a mini-surge that will probably continue through January. Because reporting and interest in general have tailed off, no one has a good idea how many cases are actually occurring, but there are enough that hospitalizations have doubled since autumn.

However, for most, COVID-19 is no longer the serious infection it was in the four previous years. After more than one million deaths in those four years — in terms of overall American casualties, think 20 Vietnam Wars, three World War IIs or two Civil Wars — the projection was that the U.S. would experience 100,000 or more deaths in 2023. Yet according to Worldometer, the actual number was just over 70,000 in 2023 and slowing in the second half of the year, as the effects of immunity and vaccination now protect the population.

For Americans today, the mortality of COVID-19 — that is, the share of people who contract the virus and die — is less than 1%, and for healthy individuals, it is significantly less than that.

When we review the effects of COVID-19 to date, we should harbor no illusions — the havoc is not merely measured in deaths and long-term disabilities. The incalculable damage wrought is everywhere: undereducated children, increases in suicides and drug overdoses, a general coarsening of society and intensified political division. This political dissonance was aggravated by the physicians and scientists who abandoned their independence during the pandemic. They let politicians exploit them to justify public policy choices.

Some lessons are being learned, albeit too late. Testifying before Congress in May 2020, Dr. Anthony Fauci, who became President Donald Trump's public health spokesperson for the pandemic, acknowledged his lack of expertise in the economic implications of societal lockdowns. Fauci devoted little attention to the unintended consequences of closing down large segments of society, a strategy advocated by most of the public health community.

Now, Francis Collins, former National Institutes of Health chief and Fauci's onetime boss at the NIH, has admitted that the public health mindset of the response to COVID-19 was a mistake.

In an interview that recently resurfaced online, Collins said, "if you're a public health person and you're trying to make a decision, you have this very narrow view of what the right decision is. And that is something that will save a life ... so you attach infinite value to stopping the disease and saving a life. You attach zero value to whether this actually totally disrupts people's lives, ruins the economy and has many kids kept out of school in a way that they never quite recover from."

This admission is a positive step forward by an influential scientist. Putting the science into perspective, Collins, a nonconformist in the scientific community, has described himself as a "serious Christian"who has attempted to bridge the gap between science and faith. That's why it was somewhat uncharacteristic that until now, he marched in lockstep with the initial zealous public health approach to limit spread of the virus through lockdowns.

Will he also admit to another serious misstep that he and Fauci committed — the attempt to silence the scientists who authored the Great Barrington Declaration, which advocated an alternative approach to confronting the pandemic? Their notion was to focus protection on the elderly and vulnerable groups, while allowing the rest of us to lead normal lives. In retrospect, the authors of the Great Barrington Declaration probably oversold their plan — the pandemic would likely have proceeded apace even with their approach, but there may have been less collateral damage. What Fauci and Collins did, however, amounted to scientific censorship and constituted a serious breach in scientific ethics: Scientists must maintain their objectivity in the search for the truth.

Many want to forget all this and move on, but no one should ignore the incalculable damage caused to our country and the rent it has put in the social fabric and our institutions. There is much to be gleaned from this, but there is a sense that rather than learn from the experience, many of the actors will attempt to rewrite their role in history to portray their actions in a more favorable light.

As the COVID-19 pandemic moves into its fifth year, it is not the beast that raged through the world in 2020 and 2021. The contagion is by no means done with us — there will likely be seasonal and sporadic outbreaks for years, and things could always change if a more lethal variant mutation pops up. For now, though, it poses little more than an inconvenience to most people and a serious threat only to an unfortunate minority. It is the whimper, not the bang, we hoped it would become.

It has been said that those who do not learn from history are condemned to repeat it. Of course, the unfortunate corollary is that even if you do learn from history, you may well be condemned to repeat it. It is only a question of time.

Index

Authors

Cory Franklin M.D. was director of medical intensive care at Cook County Hospital in Chicago for more than 25 years. An editorial board contributor to the Chicago Tribune op-ed page, his work has also appeared in the New York Times, Jerusalem Post, Chicago Sun-Times, New York Post, Guardian, Washington Post and has been excerpted in the New York Review of Books. He is the author of several books including "Cook County ICU: 30 Years of Unforgettable Patients and Odd Cases."

Robert A Weinstein M.D. is an infectious disease physician with 50 years of experience. He is a professor of internal medicine at Rush University Medical Center, former chair of medicine at Cook County Hospital, and past chief operating officer of the CORE Center for the Prevention, Care, and Research of Infectious Diseases in Chicago. Dr. Weinstein was the inaugural recipient of the CDC Lifetime Achievement Award for Infection Control and Prevention.

Mary Hall M.D. contributed to several chapters in this book. She is a pediatrician affiliated with Lurie Children's Hospital in Chicago and has served on the board of directors of Children's Community Physicians' Association.

Made in United States
Orlando, FL
04 October 2024